ARUNDEL BURNING

"We cannot afford to forget past disasters

if we are going to prevent them in the future."

Dennis L. Rubin, Fire Chief
District of Columbia

Arundel Burning

The Maryland Oyster Roast Fire of 1956

Joseph B. Ross, Jr.

THE CHESAPEAKE BOOK COMPANY
BALTIMORE, MARYLAND
2008

Library of Congress Cataloging-in-Publication Data

Ross, Joseph B., Jr.
Arundel burning : the Maryland oyster roast fire of 1956 / Joseph B. Ross, Jr.
p. cm.
Includes bibliographical references and index.
ISBN-13: 978-0-9635159-7-1 (alk. paper)
ISBN-10: 0-9635159-7-7 (alk. paper)
1. Brooklyn (Baltimore, Md.)--History--20th century. 2. Baltimore (Md.)--History--20th century. 3. Fires--Maryland--Baltimore--History--20th century. 4. Church dinners--Maryland--Baltimore--History--20th century. 5. St. Rose of Lima Catholic Church (Brooklyn, Baltimore, Md.)--History--20th century. 6. Public buildings--Fires and fire prevention--Maryland--Baltimore--History--20th century. 7. Halls--Fires and fire prevention--Maryland--Baltimore--History--20th century. 8. Disaster victims--Maryland--Baltimore--Biography. 9. Fire investigation--Maryland--Baltimore--History--20th century. 10. Anne Arundel County (Md.)--History--20th century. I. Title.
F189.B16B76 2008
975.2'71--dc22
2008031325

Manufactured in the United States of America.
The paper used in this publication meets the minimum requirements of the American National Standard for Information Sciences Permanence of Paper for Printed Library Materials ANSI Z39.48-1984.

Available wherever fine books are sold.

Distributed by Alan C. Hood & Co., Inc. P.O. Box 775, Chambersburg, PA 17201. Phone 717.267.0867. Web: www.hoodbooks.com.

For those who lost their lives,

and those who still suffer

Contents

Preface and Acknowledgments viii

Introduction xiii

1. Community and a River 3
2. Building a Fire Department 19
3. A Church Emerges from the Ashes 39
4. Oysters, Beer, and Games of Chance 47
5. Fatal Delay 56
6. Fire, Panic, and Escape 61
7. Black Snow and Crimson Skies 69
8. Survivors and Victims 86
9. Accusations and Suspicion 109
10. "I Solved These Firebug Mysteries" 127
11. Finding Answers 149
12. Black Cloud 169
13. Memories and Nightmares 184

Epilogue 191

Appendices 195

References 206

Bibliography 216

Index 219

Preface and Acknowledgments

On January 29, 1956, a raging fire devastated the Arundel Park hall in Brooklyn, Maryland. The fire killed eleven people and injured hundreds more making it the worst public assembly disaster ever to occur in Maryland. The assembly hall, located in northern Anne Arundel County and filled with people, was holding an oyster roast sponsored by Brooklyn's Saint Rose of Lima Catholic Church. The fire, which quickly spread through the large one-story, concrete-block and wooden structure destroyed lives, shattered families, devastated property, shortened livelihoods, and perpetuated the public's lack of confidence in elected officials and government bureaucracy.

There is a culture that believes tragedies similar to the Arundel Park fire can no longer occur. Unfortunately, history has a peculiar way of making that determination on its own. One only need look at the fire calamity that occurred in February 2003, at The Station night club in West Warwick, Rhode Island. Approximately one hundred people died and many more were injured when pyrotechnics were illegally discharged and ignited combustible sound-proofing foam and ceiling tile. The result was a ravaging fire that quickly spread throughout the one-story structure packed with people.[1]

Still, there have been strong initiatives, numerous changes, and significant improvements to fire regulations over the past fifty years. Today, fire and building codes address and regulate flame spread ratings on interior finishes such as ceiling tile and wall paneling. Emergency lighting is required in all public buildings. Concealed areas above ceilings are fire-stopped to reduce horizontal fire spread. Automatic sprinkler and fire alarm systems are required in most assembly occupancies. There is no doubt that these code improvements, if implemented before January 1956, would have changed the outcome of the Arundel Park fire.

Automatic sprinklers, properly installed, tested, maintained, serviced, and working in combination with early warning smoke detection systems, are the most modern engineering achievement we have for combating fires and saving lives. Today most businesses, including retail stores and places of assembly, are protected by these systems, but across the country over the past seven years a number of buildings protected by sprinkler systems have been destroyed by fire. In Maryland two were located in Bowie and Maryland

City, not far from Arundel Park. Fortunately, no one was killed or injured in either fire. But the question remains; when and where will the next system fail? Will it be in one of our large multi-screen movie theaters packed with children on a Saturday afternoon? Could it occur in one of our schools? Is it possible that sprinkler system failure could result in another Arundel Park fire tragedy or even worse, a fire similar to the Warwick disaster? These issues must constantly be addressed.

Fire protection is not just the fire department's problem. It should be addressed through an extensive partnership that includes the community and the private sector forged by training, education, enforcement, and competency.

Since January 29, 1956, Anne Arundel County, Maryland, has posted an outstanding record in regard to safety from fire in public buildings. I hope this story of the Arundel Park fire serves to promote and raise the level of the public's fire safety awareness to make sure the record stays that way. I also hope that other communities across the nation struggling with the costs, maintenance, and stringency of fire regulations and code enforcement will benefit from lessons learned in this story.

In my numerous contacts with survivors of the fire, I am astonished at their strong desire to have their story told. As they discussed the events of that tragic day with me, I was overwhelmed by the abundance of information and detail they remembered and revealed. They speak as though the fire occurred only yesterday. Fortunately for this work they believe as I do that information about the fire should be available for people to read, to question, and to apply its lessons to everyday life. In other words, they should become educated about fire safety.

The survivors have impressed upon me that people must be reminded to check access to exits and exit doors at public assemblies. They believe as I do that the public must know that if they find a locked exit door or see an unlit exit sign, or notice a discharged fire extinguisher, or think any other fire protection device is unusable or unsafe there is a process to follow for notifying authorities. That way, the community becomes a responsible entity under the fire protection partnership.

The survivors believe the book will become a lasting legacy from which people will gain knowledge. The work will reflect on the lives of the fire's victims and recognize the heroic efforts of a number of the community's hardworking citizens. It will explain what happened, why it happened, and what measures should be taken so that it never happens again.

The Arundel Park fire is an intriguing and, unfortunately, a very sad story, but this book will go beyond the fire. It will touch on the origins of Brooklyn and discuss how this community evolved from little villages and hamlets along the Patapsco River to become a major residential and industrial component of the Baltimore metropolitan area. It will describe how fire became a frequent adversary to Brooklyn's Saint Rose of Lima Catholic Church and reveal how the church demonstrated great resilience and strength as it emerged from the ashes and debris again and again.

Additionally, the book will recognize a group of very community-minded citizens who saw fire as a threat to their daily lives. Their unselfish efforts started the Brooklyn Volunteer Fire Department in 1910 and later its sister organization, the Brooklyn Community Fire Department in the late 1930s. The book will also focus on a special individual who ran a two-person fire prevention bureau office in Anne Arundel County in the early 1950s and his tireless efforts, which created the foundation for the outstanding fire service that would follow.

Finally the book will reveal how local and national events impact one another. It will also demonstrate how community, politics, religion and social aspects unfold, interweave, combine and, sometimes untangle to explain the events surrounding the Arundel Park fire.

THIS BOOK IS A STORY OF PEOPLE and the community they built, its origins and deep roots, its faith and struggle with adversity, and its strength in the face of devastation. It is a story of loss and sorrow, negligence and tenacity, shame and heroism. Such a work cannot be created without generous assistance. I am in debt to many, for it is their story. I am just the messenger.

It gives me great pleasure to recognize the following people for their help, advice, encouragement and, more importantly, their eyewitness accounts of events: Harry W. Klasmeier, Frank Kvech III, Lorretta Kane Dove, Harry Zlotowski, Leona and Charlie Doegen, Jean and Les Helfrich, Frank Homberg Jr., William Morrison, George Mills, Norman Ray, John Anderson, Rae (Utz) Bathgate, Michael Ripnick, Dr. Randall McLaughlin,

John "Jerry" and Nancy (Brady) Thompson, John "Bill" Brady, George Feeley, Iris (Peg) and Joseph (Rozmarynowski) Ross.

I would also like to thank the following Anne Arundel County Fire Department firefighters and officers, present and retired, for generously sharing with me information about the fire, and for their support and encouragement: Gary Utz, Melvin Morrison, Raymond W. Smith, Tom German, John Michael Hoy, Mike Wiley, James Amrhein, James Swinimer, Melvin Thomas, Ron Bierman, Keith Hammack, and Patrick Prendergast. In addition I would like to thank long-time Brooklyn Park residents Deborah Dyszel, Edie (Thompson) Hopla, Nancy Cadden, Father Joseph O'Meara of the Saint Rose of Lima Church, and Dr. John Bryan, former professor and faculty head of the University of Maryland's Fire Protection Engineering Program for their assistance.

Members of the Maryland Fire and Rescue Institute (MFRI) have offered encouragement, support, editorial advice and technical support: Director Steve Edwards and former director John Hoglund, Special Programs Manager Darl "Mickey" McBride, Karen Haje, Caitlin Evans, Mike Kernan, Roger Simonds, and my lovely wife Kathy Ross. Recently retired MFRI Institute Development Specialist and consultant Gloria Bizjak painstaking addressed all of my flawed writing mechanics and greatly assisted me in producing sentences that would shock my twelfth-grade English teacher. I can't thank Gloria enough.

I would also like to thank retired chief Charlie Steele and retired firefighters Sonny Tyler and Fred Reppenhagen Jr. of the Annapolis City Fire Department. These former firefighters provided information on Annapolis's contribution on the night of the fire.

Others to whom I am deeply grateful are Captain Harry Steiner of the Anne Arundel County Fire Department and private fire investigation consultant for his graphic/drawing recreations of the Arundel Park facility. State Fire Marshal William "Bill" Barnard and Bruce Hisley, retired Anne Arundel County division chief and National Fire Academy instructor, both shed light on the role of county and state in fire prevention regulations during the late 1950s and early 1960s. Bill also was helpful in providing information about some of the key participants representing the Maryland State Police.

Two Anne Arundel County officials have greatly contributed to this work. Judy Holmes, administrative secretary of the county council, assisted me in researching the notes of the county commissioners' meetings from the late 1940s and early 1950s. Inspection and Permits Code Enforcement Officer Bill Bryant provided me with a copy of the 1939 Anne Arundel County Building Code for review.

Lt. Tim Runkles of the Anne Arundel County Fire Department shared his extensive collection of fire-related historical materials, which was very helpful to this work. Deputy Fire Chief Michael Defina Jr., of the Reagan National Airport, Metropolitan Washington Airports Authority Fire and Rescue Department, along with his colleague Joseph MacDonald, provided information from their extensive collection of fire apparatus pictures and fire protection documents from the 1950s.

Laura Cleary, Coordinator, Maryland Room, Marylandia and Rare Books/ National Trust Library, University of Maryland, was intrumental in navigating me through the numerous old Baltimore *News-American* photographs now owned and generously provided by the Hearst Corporation.

Civil War historian and publisher Dan Toomey and Mark Shatz of the Ann Arrundell County Historical Society, provided needed support for this work. Jeff Korman of the Enoch Pratt Free Library's Maryland Department was very resourceful in providing maps of northern Anne Arundel County from the early 1950s. I cannot offer enough thanks to my editor, publisher, and friend Robert I. "Ric" Cottom, who believed in this project and provided encouragement and guidance.

Last but no less importantly, I want to thank Bill Wagner, writer for the *Capital Gazette,* former editor Bob Mosier, and former staff reporter Penny Riordan for their support and for giving me the "key" and countless hours of access to the newspaper's archives.

A small group of eyewitnesses to the fire wanted to remain anonymous for this work but nevertheless provided invaluable information and detail. You know who you are, and to you I extend my profound thanks. Your experiences on the night of January 29, 1956, are woven into those of a fictional surrogate family named Sokolis.

Joseph B. Ross, Jr.
Linthicum, Maryland
July 2008

Introduction

IMAGINE YOURSELF IN A SEA of frantic uncertainty. You are just one whitecap, one body bobbing in waves made up of hundreds of panic-stricken people. You are bound together by only one fearful thought—get out now! But unlike a sea there is no water; there is only the fear as bright orange and red flames laced with dark, deadly, acrid smoke roll unopposed over your head across a massive ceiling.

Your fear heightens when you find that the closest exit door is locked. Behind you, in front of you, and all around you men, women, and children are pushing, screaming, and knocking one another to the floor. Finally, you are within twenty feet of another exit door, but the sea is no longer moving. The door is jammed with frantic people fighting for fresh air and safety. Heat from the fire is now searing the back of your head, your neck, your shoulders. Your elbows sting as if you have a severe case of sunburn. The aching in the middle of your stomach is telling you that something is dreadfully wrong.

Breaking glass and the crackling fire intermix with screams and crying. Those are the sounds you hear as the anxious and frightened make a last desperate attempt to climb out the building's windows. Thick smoke makes your eyes water. In that haze, all you can do is follow the crowd. As you move in what seems like slow motion, your heart is pounding. Then, as if the past thirty seconds haven't been frightening enough, the lights go out.

The fire just described occurred a little more than fifty years ago just outside the Baltimore City's southern boundary in the Brooklyn Park area of northern Anne Arundel County. This tragic and devastating fire occurred at the Arundel Park Hall at approximately 5:05 P.M. on a cold, foggy, drizzly Sunday evening on January 29, 1956.[1] Ten people perished and an eleventh died later from severe burns. Hundreds more were injured. A one-time skating rink, the facility at the time of the fire was best known for its crab feasts, bull and oyster roasts, nightly bingo games, and the many slot machines located throughout the building.

Fifty years later, many questions still remain. What was the cause of the fire? Was organized crime involved? Why the delay to evacuate people and call the fire department? Why the mass panic? Why were exits locked? Why did people, after making their escape from the burning building, go back inside only to die in the calamity? Why were firefighters unable to put out the fire? Was the building legally constructed? What were the contributing factors that resulted in the deaths and injuries?

Most people can't remember what they did last week, let alone fifty years ago. At five years old, I have vivid memories of going up to the bedroom on the second floor of our row home on 5th Avenue in Brooklyn Park to watch the fire with my mother. I remember standing on top of a chair and looking out of the window as she pointed out the bright orange flames and dark smoke in the distance.

Eleven years later, in April 1967 when I joined the Community Fire Company, Inc. in nearby Linthicum as a volunteer firefighter, it was not long before I made a nuisance of myself questioning the older firefighters, veterans of the Arundel Park fire, about the operational facts and details of the incident. Eventually I began to collect a personal library of the fire consisting of copies of official reports, pictures, and newspaper clippings. As I continued my career as a firefighter, instructor, and officer with the Anne Arundel County Fire Department, I never passed up an opportunity to learn more about the fire. On numerous occasions, I conducted informal interviews with people associated with the fire and other firefighters who had been at the scene on that dreadful Sunday evening. Over the years, I have studied all of the reports, interview notes, film footage, photos, and newspaper articles. This is the result of that labor.

ARUNDEL BURNING

1

A Community and a River

Until a cold and rainy Sunday in January 1956, Maryland had not experienced a deadly fire at a place of public assembly. Numerous houses caught fire, particularly in Baltimore. Fires also struck the city's businesses, warehouses, and factories. At times they were spectacular, lighting up the night's sky in orange and red or sending up huge columns of thick, black smoke that could be seen for miles on a clear day. Fires of all types were fewer in the growing suburbs of Baltimore and Washington.

More importantly, few Marylanders lost their lives in fires. Fanned by a brisk, icy wind with thirty mile-per-hour gusts, the Great Baltimore Fire of February 7 and 8, 1904, consumed 140 acres of the central business district, destroying 1,526 buildings and causing over $100 million in damage, but, miraculously, only one man is known to have perished in the conflagration. Fifty years later, on February 15, 1955, fire consumed the Tru-Fit Clothing Store on Baltimore Street. The building's collapse killed six firefighters and injured another twenty, but no civilians were hurt.[1]

Maryland was a fortunate exception to a national trend. Deadly fires in churches, restaurants, theaters, and nightclubs had occurred in cities large and small, particularly around the turn of the century, when cities, including Baltimore, were crowded with densely packed wooden buildings and lacked reliable water systems. Chicago experienced the deadly Iroquois Theater fire in 1903 that killed 602 and injured another 250, including many children on holiday. In 1908 a fire struck the opera house in Boyertown, Pennsylvania,

In the 1950s, years of prosperity in postwar Baltimore, Brooklyn was an expanding community in rapidly growing Anne Arundel County. Here, members of the Brooklyn Volunteer Fire Department clean Engine #2. From left: Norman Thomas, "Smoky," Jim Rhodes, Frank Homberg, and Fred Evans. Photograph ca. 1956. (Courtesy of the Hearst Corporation.)

leaving 170 dead, including entire families, in that tiny community. Another fire killed 492 people at Boston's Coconut Grove nightclub in 1942.[2] Events like these had never occurred in Maryland, especially not in the slow, peaceful Patapsco River Valley southwest of the quiet town of Brooklyn.

Deadly public assembly fires years ago and hundreds of miles away didn't concern Frank Homberg on this Saturday in June 1955, as he positioned the big, red, pumper truck near a pond at a huge gravel pit about a thousand yards east of the Patapsco. Forty-one years old and a seventeen-year veteran "engineman," or operator/driver, for the Brooklyn Volunteer Fire Department, Frank just wanted to complete the pumper's annual service test. He had brought along some sixteen- to eighteen-year-old volunteer firefighters, some of whom would have an opportunity to operate a hose and nozzle for the first time.[3]

It was a warm morning, and Frank knew that in a couple of hours the hot humid air typical of the Chesapeake would be soaking their light summer clothing in sweat. Today he wouldn't order the young volunteers to wear their heavy turn-out coats, only helmets, gloves and boots. "Come on," Frank shouted, in a voice weathered by years of firefighting. "We need to get the hard tubes into the water before it gets too damned hot!" The inexperienced young men obediently took positions beside the engine to lift off the heavy hard rubber suction tubes, connect them, and place them in the water.

The pond was one of several in the swampy valley of the Patapsco just south of the Baltimore City line, very near the community of Brooklyn. In the early nineteenth century, Maryland's Patapsco River Valley had been considered a source of beauty and commerce. The river originates in tributaries cascading down the fall line in central Maryland between picturesque Westminster and Reisterstown, and flows southeasterly for forty miles to Baltimore's huge and busy port, where it becomes one of the headwaters of the Chesapeake.[4] "Patapsco" is an a Algonquian name passed down from the Indians who inhabited this part of Maryland four hundred years ago. It means "blackwater" and "white capped waves."[5] Three hundred and fifty years ago, Captain John Smith observed and noted the river during one of his sailing expeditions from Jamestown. In the seventeenth century, ships could navigate as far as Elkridge, approximately nine miles upstream, but over time the river silted in places, and by the early 1800s navigation to

The Brooklyn Volunteer Fire Department's Engine #1 drafting water from a pond near Belle Grove Road in the vicinity of Brooklyn. Such operations were necessary in a county with minimal infrastructure, including fire hydrants. (Charlie Doegen and Les Helfrich.)

Elkridge was no longer possible.[6] Its natural inland harbor made Baltimore the port closest to the Ohio Valley, and spurred its growth. Where it is widest near the harbor, the river forms the boundary that separates Maryland's Baltimore and Anne Arundel Counties.

The east bank of the Patapsco, the Anne Arundel County side, was known as Brooklyn and Brooklyn Park. Here, local sand and gravel companies created ponds by digging out the valuable and abundant sand deposits that were deep beneath the marsh grass. Light brown, wide-bladed grass, two to four feet high, and "cattails" spreading from marshy lowlands and other ponds, surrounded the little mound of solid ground on which Frank and the "boys" had just about finished connecting the hard tubes. The tubes would serve as a conduit as the engine captured and pumped the pond water.

With the engine idling, a very focused Frank Homberg now shifted the control levers that would engage the pump from a power take off unit located in the truck's transmission. He pulled another lever, activating a smaller electric piston pump that exhausted the air from the main pump. The piston pump made a sound like a fog horn as it started. Gathered in a semi-circle near the truck's pump operations panel, the young volunteers marveled at the way Frank manipulated all of the levers and controls. They watched the glass-covered pressure gauges on the control panel intently as the little black needles inside fluctuated and dropped below zero.

As the piston pump drew the air from the main pump chamber, gravity forced the cool pond water up through the hard tubes and into the pump. "Come on baby, don't let me down," Frank thought to himself. Carefully he watched the gauges and slowly throttled up the engine from another control on the panel to accelerate the truck's mighty centrifugal pump. A tense moment followed, as the needles on the panels gauges fluttered and slowly began to rise above zero. Even a small air leak within the pump's piping or hard suction tubes could interfere with this operation. The needle rose steadily. The pump's impeller, encased in a steel chamber, rotated at hundreds of revolutions per minute. Frank increased the engine speed and smoothly transformed the calm pond water into a beautiful white stream from a large "deluge" nozzle mounted on the top of the truck. It shot fifty feet into the warm air, over and onto the far side of the pond.

The Brooklyn fire pumper, a 1947 open-cab Mack, was the newest fire truck in the department's fleet. As it drafted and pumped water from a pond along this old dirt power line road about a quarter-mile west of Belle Grove Road, the young volunteer firefighters imagined they were applying a magnificent pattern of water on a major structure fire.[7]

The spray created a rainbow in the morning sun. Looking through it, Frank saw a dump truck and a couple of cars driving along Belle Grove Road. This two-lane highway, which intersects with Potee, Hanover Street, and Ritchie Highway north at the Baltimore City line, runs south approximately half a mile east of and parallel to the Patapsco River. Belle Grove Road makes up the northern section of State Route 170, connecting Baltimore City with the Odenton–Fort George G. Meade area approximately twelve miles to the south. The highway is one of Brooklyn's main thoroughfares.

The needle on the pumper's pressure gauge now registered 150 pounds per square inch. Frank had the boys pull off a few more hose lines with attached nozzles, and before long the engine was discharging water at its rated 750 gallons per minute. Frank lifted the hot metal hood covering

Governor Ritchie Highway was considered the nation's most modern highway when it opened in 1936. This Baltimore News-American *photograph was taken in June 1952 from newly built Harundale, on the southbound lane near the present Farmington Road intersection. (Courtesy of the Hearst Corporation.)*

the roaring engine and propped open the covers with a metal rod to allow cooling air into the engine compartment. He also noticed a light coat of dust covering the truck's bright red paint. "Hell," he thought, "its going to take me until late afternoon to clean up this wagon."

About noon, Frank's service test of "Brooklyn No. 2," was completed and the truck was ready to return to the fire station on the corner of Ritchie Highway and 11th Avenue. The tee shirts he and the volunteers wore were saturated with sweat. It had been a productive morning, Frank thought.

As he drove north on the hard surface of Belle Grove Road, he passed the Arundel Park complex and the Matlack Trucking Company on his right before reaching the crest of the hill near 6th Avenue. As the road leveled out, he shifted into a higher gear, and the truck picked up speed, refreshing the sweaty volunteers who were holding on to a metal bar and standing on the truck's back step.

As the pumper continued toward the city line, the new brick, one-story Belle Grove Elementary School appeared on the west side of the road. North of the school were mostly brick row homes that lined the roads from the school to the city line. Along the east side of Belle Grove were larger, older, and more detailed houses. These wood frame homes are situated on avenues that stretch west to east connecting Belle Grove Road with Governor Ritchie Highway.

"Ritchie Highway," as it was and still is called, was opened in 1936.[8] At the time considered the nation's most modern highway, it consisted of two lanes running north and two lanes running south separated by a wide, grassy median. The highway, designed in a straight line with only one ninety-degree turn, begins at the city line in Brooklyn where Hanover and Potee Streets intersect. It terminates approximately thirty miles south on the north shore of the Severn River at the picturesque U.S. Naval Academy bridge on Maryland Route 450 near the historic campus in Annapolis. The new roadway, designated Maryland State Route 2, was named for Maryland's beloved Governor Albert Cabell Ritchie, one of the state's greatest leaders and a champion of public works who served four consecutive terms. A man of enormous political stature, he was considered a Democratic presidential hopeful at the party's convention in 1932 but lost the nomination to a governor from New York named Franklin Roosevelt.[9]

Frank pulled the truck with its tired young crew into the parking lot of the ESSO station on the southeast corner of Belle Grove Road and Ritchie Highway. Attendants and customers alike stopped what they were doing to admire the huge red machine. Small children waved their arms and happily called to the firemen. Frank gave each of the volunteers a nickel to buy a bottle of coke and asked the attendant to fill the truck's forty-gallon tank. The bill for ten dollars' worth of gasoline would be charged to an account the fire company maintained with the gas station.[10]

With one eye on the young firefighters who were now playfully hitting and grabbing each other at the soda machine, Frank looked up Ritchie Highway. Along the highway and its side streets were large two-and-a-half story wooden houses with wide green lawns that rolled down the hillsides and terminated at the sidewalks. The communities on the south side of the city line that ran through Brooklyn were established as Brooklyn Park and Brooklyn Heights.

With the gas tank filled, Frank drove the engine up Ritchie Highway and backed it onto the narrow concrete apron in front of the station so it faced the busy southbound lane. Soon the truck was covered with water and soap as Frank, the young volunteers, and others scrubbed and hosed down Brooklyn Engine No. 2.

Near the Brooklyn Fire Department's drafting site at the pond along the old dirt power line road, the Belle Grove Road corridor is a mixed residential, rural, and light industrial community. The southernmost segment of the road runs through the African-American village known as Pumphrey before becoming Camp Meade Road at the intersection with Baltimore-Annapolis Boulevard. Camp Meade Road becomes Telegraph Road in Severn and the final stretch of Maryland Route 170.

In the middle of the Belle Grove Road corridor the terrain rolls into something like a valley. Along the valley's southern rim is an elevated wooded area, with a commanding view of Baltimore City. Here the land slopes from the south to the northwest, leveling off along a flat, sparsely wooded plain that runs all the way to the Patapsco River half a mile to the west. It is on this plain at the foot of the wooded slope along Belle Grove Road that Arundel Park was located, together with several other rural/light-industrial complexes.

In addition to a main hall, Arundel Park's complex included a barn and a couple of other structures on the hall's southeast side. Just to the north and on the same side of the street was the one-story garage and office complex of the Matlack Trucking Company. The lot surrounding the terminal was full of truck tractors painted dark green, and shiny aluminum tank trailers.

Ten years earlier, on a sunny Monday morning in October 1945, Leroy Helms, a very successful Brooklyn businessman, had stood outside the Helms Cocktail Lounge on Patapsco Avenue and looked down the street at the busy Hanover Street intersection less than a block away. Helms knew he

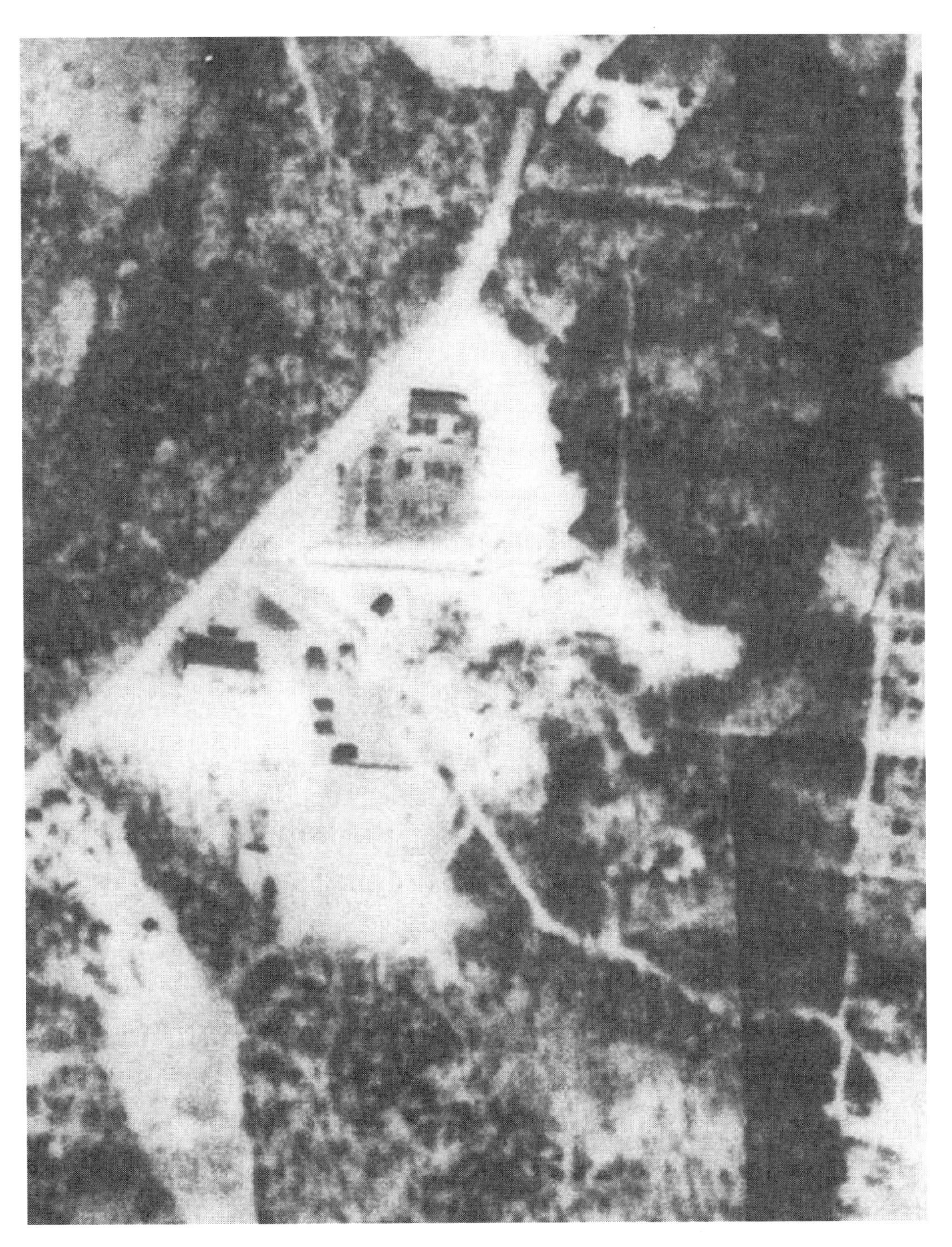

This 1953 aerial photograph of part of the Belle Grove Road corridor shows the back of the Arundel Park (center left). Note the massive Quonset-style roof. The Matlack Trucking Company is to the north (just above and right). (Courtesy of the Enoch Pratt Free Library, Central Library/State Library Resource Center, Baltimore, Maryland.)

was fortunate to operate a business and own a building so close to Brooklyn's commercial hub.

Roy, as most people called him, also might have known that Brooklyn did not just happen. The thriving community was all part of a grandiose plan. In the 1850s and during the last half of the nineteenth century, a number of villages and hamlets sprang up along the southeast side of the Patapsco River—Fairfield, Masonville, Wagner's Point, Curtis Bay, and Hawkins Point, as well as Brooklyn—and made up the most northern section of Anne Arundel County.[11]

On April 26, 1853, Maryland's General Assembly incorporated the "Patapsco Company" and authorized it to deal in real estate in northern Anne Arundel County. Made up of businessmen from Baltimore and local landowners, the company soon laid out plans for a new town. An employee by the name of R. W. Templeman is said to have suggested the name Brooklyn after its New York counterpart, which was separated from New York City by the East River, much as the Patapsco separated Anne Arundel County from Baltimore.[12]

Three years later, the 4,750-foot wooden "Light Street" toll bridge was constructed over the Patapsco River. Stretching from Brooklyn's northwest tip to the mainland of Baltimore City, the bridge greatly enhanced transportation and communication between the city and Arundel's new development. Now connected with all of the benefits and amenities of big city opportunity, the Brooklyn community began to expand and thrive.[13]

By 1878 the prosperous and ambitious Baltimore and Ohio Railroad extended service from its hub in Baltimore to Brooklyn's factories, businesses, and docks, and east to the community of Curtis Bay with its businesses and waterfront shipping terminals. The railroad, street car service—and the state's purchase of the Light Street Bridge and elimination of all tolls—bolstered the town's economic potential. The busy intersection of Hanover Street and Patapsco Avenue became Brooklyn's town center and central business district.[14]

Leroy "Roy" Helms turned around and opened the front door of his building. Behind the door was a stairway to the second floor apartments. Roy and his wife Annie shared the largest and rented out the others. The couple would remain there until they built a larger home less then two miles away on Ritchie Highway in Brooklyn Park.[15] In addition to the Helms

The Light Street Toll Bridge, built in 1856 across the Patapsco to connect Anne Arundel County with Baltimore, greatly enhanced communications and transportation between Baltimore and Brooklyn. In 1915 a fire practically destroyed it. (Brooklyn-Curtis Bay Historical Committee.)

Cocktail Lounge and the apartments on the second floor, the building at 116–118 Patapsco Avenue also housed Stewart Motors.

Roy opened the door to the apartment and grabbed the car keys lying on a lamp table. Today he had to drive into downtown Baltimore to pick up supplies for the cocktail lounge. When he arrived at the Hanover Street bridge, traffic was stopped and the drawbridge span was raised. "Oh great," he thought. "How long is this going to take?" While he waited on the bridge with the rest of the morning rush hour traffic, he recalled stories he had heard regarding an older wooden bridge that ran between Light Street and Brooklyn.

One told of a 1913 tragedy when a streetcar traveling over the wooden bridge derailed and plunged into the river, killing a man. Another had it that two years after the streetcar accident a bad fire partially destroyed the bridge. As a result of the accident and fire, plans were drawn for a wider, stronger, and safer structure. The new concrete Hanover Street drawbridge, costing $1,250,000.00, opened in 1917. The old wooden Light Street Bridge closed for good.[16]

The newer Hanover Street Bridge on the left and the old Light Street Bridge on the right just before its demolition. Photograph ca. 1917. (Courtesy of the Hearst Corporation.)

According to his granddaughter, Loretta Kane Dove, Roy was hard-working, a loving grandfather, and a man who enjoyed the good times at the Helms Cocktail Lounge. She remembers him telling stories of a sailor, named Arthur Godfrey, stationed at Curtis Bay Coast Guard Yard on Pennington Avenue in the 1940s, who played his ukulele at the quaint little tavern. No one knew then that the ukulele player who frequented the community's "hot spot" at the corner of Second Street and the north side of Patapsco Avenue, would go on to become the legendary "Arthur Godfrey" of radio and television fame.[17]

Another patron was Gordon Ripnick, who worked at the Bethlehem Shipyard as an electrician before joining the Marines during World War II. He saw action at the battle for Okinawa in 1945 as a radar operator spotting Japanese aircraft, particularly kamikazes. After the war, he found work as an electrical inspector for the Navy in Baltimore's busy shipyards. Living where he had grown up, in his father's house in the 500 block of Patapsco Avenue, only three blocks from the tavern, he helped Roy Helms rid the tavern of troublemakers who had had too much to drink. Most had strayed in from other bars in nearby Curtis Bay or South Baltimore.

One evening while Gordon was in the tavern, a particular patron from South Baltimore caught his eye, and he did everything in his power to keep her from leaving. Her name was Mary Timbs. Eventually he won her heart, and in 1949 they married. In the early 1950s, Gordon and Mary had two children and purchased a new two-story Cape Cod–style house on 6th Avenue, near Belle Grove Road in Brooklyn Park.[18]

The Helms family was blessed with a keen business sense. Roy's wife Annie owned and operated the Please All Beauty Shop on the east side of Hanover Street, directly across from Read's Drug Store. Willie Helms, Roy's brother, owned and operated a tavern next to the Ben Franklin Five and Dime on Hanover Street. The building that housed the "five and dime" on the first floor had a bowling alley on the second floor.[19]

In the mid-1940s, Roy and his associates believed it was time to expand and take on a larger venture. They developed plans for a new building at 4901 Belle Grove Road to be known as Arundel Park, and formed the Arundel Park Corporation, Inc. Its officers were George Stump, president; Leroy Helms, vice president and treasurer; and Robert Middlekauff, secretary. Construction of the large hall, designed by the engineering firm of Kubitz and Koenig to be 160 feet long and 80 feet wide, began in 1949. Claus Brothers Construction Company of Glen Burnie was contracted to build the massive structure.[20]

The main hall was completed in 1950. A kitchen, cocktail lounge, milk bar (at which customers could buy milkshakes, ice cream sodas, hamburgers and fries), restrooms, offices, storage rooms, and cloak rooms were added later.[21] A large white sign with dark lettering in front of the parking lot along the curb of Belle Grove Road read, "ARUNDEL PARK, DRIVE IN, BAR BQ, ICE CREAM-22 FLAVORS, OPEN DAILY 8 AM – 12 PM, DAILY SPECIALS, REAL HOME COOKED MEALS." A smaller sign, painted dark with light lettering and just south of the larger one read, "HELMS PARK COCKTAIL LOUNGE – SEAFOOD."[22]

Long-time Brooklyn Park resident Michael Ripnick has fond memories of his grandfather, Gordon Ripnick, taking him and his brother Richard to the milk bar on Saturday afternoons for a milkshake or a sundae. Only five years old at the time, Michael still remembers the enormity of the place and the red and white paneled metal awnings that protected the entrances and doorways.[23]

Beginning in 1950 the establishment served as a small amusement park, skating rink, and bingo hall and held numerous oyster and bull roasts and crab feasts. With more than thirteen thousand square feet of floor space, it was northern Anne Arundel County's largest covered-floor area. Churches, fraternal organizations and athletic clubs rented the hall for various functions and to raise money.[24] In addition to roasts, Arundel Park sponsored nightly bingo games. Every Tuesday, Friday, and Saturday night, people from all around the region attended, hoping to win a jackpot of fifty dollars. On special occasions a new car was offered as a prize. Arundel Park provided buses to pick up customers and take them home after the games.

The restaurant, which included carry-out service and a cocktail lounge, was open seven days a week. A hungry customer could have fresh ham and sauerkraut for seventy-five cents, or a roast beef dinner for ninety-five cents.

The facility largely complied with fire prevention code requirements then in existence. It was equipped with portable fire extinguishers, and exit doors were equipped with panic hardware. Illuminated exit signs were attached inside over exit doorways. At its own expense, the Arundel Park

Corporation installed a fire hydrant south of the hall to provide water in the event of a fire.[25]

Unfortunately, although the park met the requirements of the fire prevention code, it did not meet the fire protection requirements in the county's building code—a different set of regulations that covered the materials used in construction, sprinkler and standpipe systems, and area restrictions, all of which can affect a fire's ability to spread and public safety.[26] Those issues apparently were not given serious consideration when Arundel Park was designed and constructed. But they would figure prominently in the sort of tragedy that, until the evening of January 29, 1956, only happened years ago in towns and cities many miles away from the small community of Brooklyn, Maryland.

With his underwriter's experience and knowledge of the county's fire protection capacities, Harry Klasmeier was the right person to become Anne Arundel County's first fire marshal. Here he is pictured with his treasured 1920s vintage Baltimore City Arhens-Fox fire engine in 1967. (Courtesy of the Hearst Corporation.)

2

The Building of a Fire Department

Conflagration is a term professionals use to describe fires that spread from building to building, engulf large areas covered with structures, or consume hundreds of acres of forest. They typically occur during long periods of dry weather and are usually accompanied by heavy wind. At the turn of the century, terrible fires were not uncommon. Conflagrations famously occurred in Chicago (1871), Baltimore (1904), and San Francisco (1906) following the great earthquake.[1] The first decade of the twentieth century saw destructive conflagrations in Chelsea, Massachusetts (1908), Paterson, New Jersey (1902), and Jacksonville, Florida (1901).[2] American cities, towns, and villages took fire very seriously. Brooklyn, Maryland, was no different. The town formed the Brooklyn Volunteer Fire Department in 1910 and the next year spent $5,990 to build a two-story brick and wood fire station at 5th Street and Pontiac Avenue. This bucket brigade fire department soon acquired a tank wagon pulled by farm horses. According to Harry Junker, one of the department's original members, the horses were borrowed from William Huber who lived on Pontiac Avenue and 4th Street.[3]

Fire alarm boxes were placed strategically throughout Brooklyn's orderly, tree-lined streets. When the pulling mechanism was activated, the box telegraphed a signal to the new fire station. The signal printed out on a ticker tape the street location of the alarm box and simultaneously activated

Members of the Brooklyn Volunteer Fire Department with their tank/chemical fire fighting wagon on the Pontiac Avenue side of the two-story brick fire station located on Fifth Street, about 1910. The building still stands. (Charlie Doegen and Les Helfrich.)

the siren in the fire station's cupola. In addition to providing fire protection, the station became a community landmark. Meetings, dances, and other fundraisers were held on the station's second floor.

As Brooklyn's businesses and manufacturing plants flourished along the waterfront, other developments were taking place forty miles to the south in the state capital at Annapolis. Political leaders were making significant changes to the Baltimore map. In 1919, the General Assembly passed legislation to allow Baltimore City to annex more than sixty square miles of adjacent metropolitan area, including the towns of Brooklyn, Curtis Bay, Fairfield, Wagner's Point, and Hawkins Point.[4]

For the members of Brooklyn's Volunteer Fire Department, the 1919 annexation brought about major change. The city disbanded the volunteers and replaced them with around-the-clock professional crews. The new Baltimore City company operating out of the station at 5th Street and Pontiac Avenue became Engine 35, consisting of a 1912 Mack AB (Jr.) chassis with combination Hose Wagon Body. Truck Company 21, a Mack AC chassis with a used Holloway city service ladder truck body, would join Engine 35 almost two years later, after renovations were made so the station could accommodate the longer vehicle.[5]

Across the street from the fire station lived an enthusiastic boy named Joseph W. Neil. Joe would often hang around the firehouse, helping the firefighters clean the rigs and listening while they told exciting stories of responding to alarms and fighting fires. Years later he would grow up, move to Brooklyn Park, and become a firefighter himself.[6]

Fire protection was not a service provided solely by Baltimore City. As towns and villages in its surrounding rural counties grew, numerous other volunteer fire departments came into existence. In February 1936 a number of civic-minded citizens living on the Anne Arundel County side of Brooklyn gathered and formed the Brooklyn Community Fire Department. John K. Culver deeded the site at the corner of 11th Avenue

Brooklyn VFD Engine #1—1938 US Fire Apparatus—in front of the station at the southwest corner of Ritchie Highway and 11th Avenue. This engine was the first to arrive at the Arundel Park Fire eighteen years later. (Gary Utz.)

Phone, Prospect 1070 | Fire Call Only: Prospect 241

Brooklyn Community Volunteer Fire Co., Inc.

Governor Ritchie Highway and Eleventh Avenue

BROOKLYN, MARYLAND

WILLIAM G. BAUER, Chief

BOARD OF GOVERNORS

ROLAND BROSEKER,
President

B. W. McDONALD,
Vice-President

E. HOMBERG,
Treasurer

ELTON E. HEA,
Secretary

MEMBER:
National Fire Protection Assn.
Maryland State Firemen's Assn.
Anne Arundel County Volunteer Firemen's Assn.
Chiefs' Club of Maryland
Eastern Assn. of Fire Chiefs
International Assn. of Fire Chiefs

At Your Service—24 Hours a Day

30 active, hard hitting fire fighters, every man with 2 years of training in scientific fire fighting. Graduates of the College of Engineering, University of Maryland.

25 men—ready to serve you with Ambulance Service, each man holding an advanced certificate from the Red Cross, First Aid for two years training.

A membership of 300 to back up the active fire fighters.

An active Ladies Auxiliary, beneficial to the fire department.

and Ritchie Highway for the construction of its new fire station.[7] A grant enabled the fire company to defray 80 percent of the building's original cost, and a mortgage was taken out for the balance due on the property and to purchase the company's first fire engine. The arrangement required the Anne Arundel County commissioners to put the county's annual $2,000 equipment allotment toward the mortgage.

When the new Brooklyn fire station opened its doors for operation in 1938, the community's insurance classification established by the Board of Fire Underwriters changed to "protected," and the rate dropped from 45 cents to 25 cents per hundred dollars of property valuation. The 44 percent reduction in insurance premiums for Brooklyn Park and Brooklyn Heights was welcome news for businesses and property owners.[8]

On September 8, 1938, the Brooklyn Community Volunteer Fire Department, with its new 1938 pumper truck, the "US," built by the U.S. Fire Apparatus Company of Wilmington, Delaware, was officially accepted as a member of the Maryland State Firemen's Association. The department's first chief was William G. Bauer, and at midnight on September 28, 1938, the new organization responded to its first fire, a blazing chicken coop at 307 Townsend Avenue.[9]

Shortly thereafter, Frank E. Homberg was hired as a "fire chauffeur" (a driver and pump operator) and started work on January 1, 1939, at $100 per month. Five days later, on January 6, 1939, the department was accepted as a member of the Anne Arundel County Volunteer Fireman's Association. Later that year a second driver/operator, Joseph Jager, was hired.[10]

As an employee working for the Brooklyn Fire Department and receiving a check each month from Anne Arundel County, Frank considered himself among the very fortunate—he was lucky to have a job. The country was still mired in the great Depression, and a great many men remained unemployed.

All of that was soon to change. In the late 1930s and early 1940s as war clouds appeared over Europe and Asia, unemployed men and their hungry families migrated to Baltimore from the Carolinas, West Virginia, Pennsylvania, and Kentucky in search of work. In unprecedented numbers,

Opposite: Apparatus, equipment, and members in front of the original two-bay Brooklyn VFD Fire Station, ca. 1940. (Charlie Doegen and Les Helfrich.)

Fire department communications were greatly enhanced when Engine 1 was equipped with a two-way radio to the county police department in Ferndale. The radio is demonstrated here by Sgt. William L. Brown Jr. and Officer Henry T. Arthur in Scout Car #5, on February 24, 1940. (Courtesy of the Hearst Corporation.)

they descended upon Baltimore's great port to work in the shipyards, steel mills, and manufacturing plants, which were gearing up to full capacity with a flood of war-related orders.[11]

As thousands of newcomers settled in, the appearance of Brooklyn dramatically changed. Plans for building more large, stylish, and attractive wooden single-family houses were set aside, and thousands of smaller brick rowhouses were constructed throughout Brooklyn and Curtis Bay. The emergency response activities of the new Brooklyn firefighting organization increased dramatically.

Because fire insurance underwriters required at least one paid driver on duty at all times, Homberg and Jager took turns staffing the station. One would work ten hours a day for seven days straight, while the other came in and worked fourteen hours each night. At the end of each week the two driver operators changed shifts.

People needing the services of the Brooklyn Fire Department would pick up a telephone and dial the operator. The Chesapeake and Potomac Telephone Company's Curtis Bay switchboard took the necessary information, then activated the siren on top of the fire station.[12]

Fire department communications were greatly enhanced when Engine 1, the US, was equipped with a two-way radio to the county police department in Ferndale. In order to expand the department's capabilities, it purchased an ambulance in 1941 to respond to medical emergencies. In 1942, the fire department board of directors decided it needed a second engine to back up the 1938 US and to handle additional responses. The board purchased a second engine that April.[13]

The large influx of people drawn to Baltimore's defense industries during World War II continued into the postwar years, as did the housing boom in Brooklyn. A major brick rowhouse complex was built behind a field along Ritchie Highway across the street from the Brooklyn Fire Station. It was named Victory Gardens to commemorate the war effort. Another complex east of the "Gardens" closer to Church Street was named "Arundel Village."

These new residential complexes with thousands of inhabitants meant a tremendous increase in activity for the Brooklyn fire department, as it responded to brush, trash, vehicle, shed, garage, and dwelling fires. The department's ambulance crew was also kept busy responding to heart attacks, falls, auto accident injuries, respiratory distresses, and other types of illness.

The 1950s saw two-and-a-half-story, single-family bungalows being constructed along with additional endless blocks of brick row homes along the east and west sides of Belle Grove Road. Schools and shopping centers followed. Young families armed with Veterans Assistance money from the Service Members' Readjustment Act of 1944, commonly referred to as the "GI Bill," began moving to Baltimore's quiet suburbs.[14] The suburbs promised lower property tax rates and new houses with actual grass yards in which children could play. Buying a house in Anne Arundel County was for most people the fulfillment of a dream.

In the fall of 1955 it was not uncommon to see teams of surveyors and civil engineers in the area, as plans were developed for a major highway that would be the throughway for the new Baltimore Harbor Tunnel, then under construction. Excavation for this much needed expressway was scheduled to start along the Anne Arundel County side of the Patapsco River in the spring of 1956. The new highway, whose construction would bring still more jobs to the area, would run parallel to the east side of the river.

Through the mid-1950s, Anne Arundel County's building boom accelerated. Building permits in 1955 jumped 1,360 over the previous year. According to a commissioner's report, the county saw an increase of nearly $13 million in the value of new buildings.[15]

The good life in Anne Arundel County meant access to well-paying jobs. People worked in nearby Baltimore's shipyards, shipping terminals, steel mills, rail yards, manufacturing plants, and the newly constructed Friendship International Airport. With a short commute to Baltimore and Washington and five hundred miles of shoreline for boating and swimming during the summer months, Anne Arundel County was the place to live and bring up a family.

Yet 1950s life in Brooklyn was not without its nuisances. On the Baltimore City side of the river, a large, open burning dump just east of the Cherry Hill housing projects almost daily dropped ash and the heavy odors of smoke and trash on Brooklyn Park, which was downwind. Foul smells from the chemical and manufacturing plants in Fairfield and Wagner's Point at times drifted into the Brooklyn community.

Between Baltimore and Elkridge, the beauty that had marked the Patapsco River and its bustling commerce during the earlier part of the nineteenth century had disappeared. Many nonresidential areas bordering the river had become sites for gravel pits, trash dumps, and junkyards. Drinking bars and unattractive light industrial facilities were established haphazardly along Belle Grove Road.

By January 1956, the Brooklyn Community Fire Department could boast of seventeen years of dedicated service to the people and businesses of the northern Anne Arundel County and was becoming a viable fire suppression and medical response organization in its own right. The department did not limit its responses to fires in Brooklyn. Through a mutual aid agreement with other county departments, it also answered emergencies in nearby Linthicum, Marley, Ferndale, and Glen Burnie.

Brooklyn VFD's fleet of engines and ambulances, ca. 1955. By the mid-1950s the Brooklyn Community Volunteer Fire Department was becoming a viable fire suppression and medical response organization in its own right. (Charlie Doegen and Less Helfrich.)

A mutual aid agreement was also established with the Friendship International Airport Fire Department, owned by Baltimore City and located just south of Linthicum. The agreement required the airport department to respond with firefighting units to northern sections of the county when requested. The county fire departments would reciprocate by responding to incidents at the airport.[16]

Joe Neil, the boy who years before had liked to hang around the station and listen to the firemen, had risen to chief. He had also become a remarkable administrator of department fund raisers and other sources of revenue. In addition to the 1938 US and an ambulance, the department now maintained two more pumper trucks. The newest was a 1947 Mack with a 750-gallon-per-minute (gpm) pump rating. All the pumper trucks were equipped with two-way radios that communicated with a 100-watt base transmitter and receiver at Brooklyn's fire station. On the low band 46.50

Brooklyn VFD's "Old Fire Horse," Engineman and Deputy Chief Frank Homberg (middle row, glasses and uniform cap) with his University of Maryland Fire Service Extension Basic Fire School class on the 11th Avenue side of the fire station, circa 1956. (Charlie Doegen and Les Helfrich.)

radio frequency, all county units could communicate with one another and with the fire stations.[17]

The Brooklyn Fire Department was very progressive in its firefighter training. Many of its members had been trained through the University of Maryland Fire Service Extension's (now Maryland Fire and Rescue Institute) statewide Firemen's Training Program. Engineman Frank Homberg, who

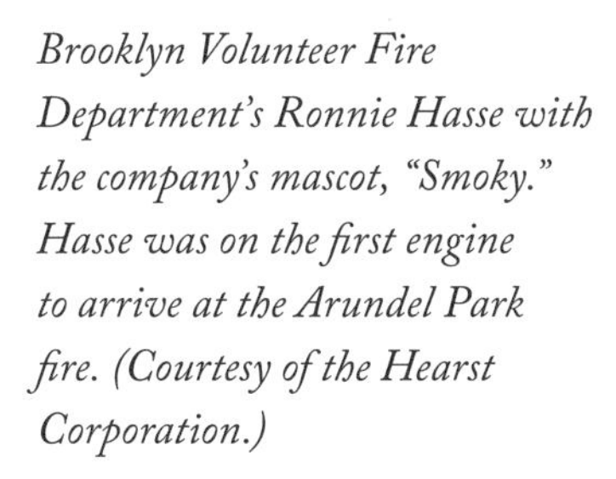
Brooklyn Volunteer Fire Department's Ronnie Hasse with the company's mascot, "Smoky." Hasse was on the first engine to arrive at the Arundel Park fire. (Courtesy of the Hearst Corporation.)

was also the volunteer deputy chief, and Lester Helfrich, a volunteer officer and driver, were now part-time fire training instructors for the fire service extension.

Leroy Helms was greatly supportive of the Brooklyn fire organization. After the Arundel Park Corporation paid to have a fire hydrant installed three hundred feet south of Arundel Park's main hall, the park complex became the site of fire training drills. (The hydrant did more than aid the fire department, it also reduced Arundel Park's insurance premium.) With permission from Arundel Park's owners and a steady supply of water, the Brooklyn Fire Department practiced hose line evolutions* in a nearby ball field and wooded area. As Deputy Chief Frank Homberg barked out orders, weary veterans and enthusiastic trainees pulled the heavy hose lines and applied and directed water fog streams at nozzle pressures of one hundred

* Hose evolutions are the best methods of pulling hose off of the engine's hose bed, moving large amounts of hose over a large area, positioning crew members along the hose line to move it, moving uncharged hose lines or lines filled with water, and attaching nozzles and other appliances to the hose.

pounds per square inch. According to Les Helfrich, the Arundel Park building was also used for practice in raising and lowering ladders during fire training drills.[18]

TWENTY-FIVE MILES DOWN Ritchie Highway in Annapolis, Church Circle with its graceful eighteenth-century buildings was visible from the large courthouse window that illuminated the very small office of the Anne Arundel County Fire Prevention Bureau. Until recently, the county's only formal fire protection organization had been the Anne Arundel County Firemen's Association, a confederation of the county's twenty-three incorporated volunteer fire stations and the five stations in Annapolis. Well aware of the need for fire prevention and safety, the association had lobbied Anne Arundel's board of county commissioners to create the fire prevention bureau.

On this day, March 12, 1955, the fire prevention bureau had been in existence for exactly eight months,[19] and thus far most of the inspector's time had been devoted to cleaning up a number of the county public school buildings, some which were clearly "fire traps."[20] But not today. As he admired the view out his window, the bureau's first and only chief fire marshal, twenty-nine-year-old Harry W. Klasmeier, contemplated taking the pleasantly long drive up Ritchie Highway to the Arundel Park facility in Brooklyn. Klasmeier was looking forward to conducting a fire inspection of the huge amusement hall.[21]

Harry Klasmeier was no stranger to fire incidents and had gained an appreciation for the dangers of firefighting at an early age. As a youngster growing up in the busy section of Baltimore bordered by Washington Boulevard and the B&O Railroad's Camden Station, he followed many fires throughout the bustling city. On October 13, 1937, at a building fire on the southwest corner of Hanover and Perry Streets, not far from his home, he watched as a three-story brick wall collapsed and buried Lt. James K. Harrison under twenty feet of rubble. Lieutenant Harrison was thirty-two, and had served nine years with the Baltimore City Fire Department.[22]

While still in his teens, Harry furthered his love for firefighting by joining the Lombardee Beach Volunteer Fire Department near his family's summer house on picturesque Stony Creek, a large body of water along the Patapsco River in Anne Arundel County. Later, in 1943, he signed

Brooklyn VFD's fire fighters train with their hard suction hose and deluge nozzle on the sports fields on the grounds of Arundel Park, circa 1956. Engineman Eddie Utz stands at far left at Engine 2's pump panel. (Charlie Doegen and Les Helfrich.)

on with the U.S. Army Air Corps and was trained as a radar specialist on B-29 "Superfortress" bombers. Fortunately the war ended before Harry saw combat. He returned to school and concentrated on his career in fire protection.

After graduating from the Johns Hopkins University in 1949 with a degree in business administration, Harry went to work for the Maryland Fire

Underwriters Rating Bureau as a fire protection engineer. Since the Bureau of Fire Underwriters studied the causes of devastating fires, inspected high-value commercial establishments for fire hazards, and tested fire protection equipment and systems, Harry became knowledgeable in fire prevention and fire inspection techniques.[23]

The Bureau of Fire Underwriters evaluated a community's fire protection by rating the proficiency of its fire companies, and their findings had an impact on local insurance rates. As a fire underwriter, Harry worked closely with the local fire companies. He became very familiar with fire pumps, fire apparatus testing and maintenance procedures, water systems, and the capabilities of the engines operating out of Anne Arundel County's fire stations. In time, he would come to learn the importance of strategically located fire stations, reliable fire apparatus and equipment, and more importantly, the need for highly trained firefighters.

Equipped with his underwriter's experience and his knowledge of the county's fire protection capabilities, smart, articulate Harry Klasmeier was the right person at the right time to take on the responsibilities of enforcing Anne Arundel County's first fire prevention code. That is why the county commissioners hired him for the position of fire marshal.

The Anne Arundel County Fire Prevention Code was a comprehensive document comprising some 104 pages and sixty-eight paragraphs. The document, which mirrored its Baltimore City counterpart, was developed by a committee of the firemen's association appointed by the county commissioners.[24]

The code either recommended or required "best practices" for preventing fire, limiting its spread, and providing exits for building occupants. For example, it required owners of business establishments to keep exit doors unlocked; to safely limit, store, and maintain flammable liquids such as gasoline, kerosene, and paint thinner in approved containers; and to establish the safe distance from a structure at which one could light a trash fire. Since most home and business owners burned trash and leaves in the 1950s, these distances would be helpful in limiting the hazards of outside fires.

The document also established the duties of the fire marshal's position, such as enforcing the code through inspections, handling complaints relating to matters of fire safety, and investigating the cause, origin and circumstances of fires. The fire marshal reviewed plans for all new commercial buildings and residential subdivisions to determine if they were in compliance with the fire code. Harry was also responsible for educating the public in all matters involving fire and its prevention.

So on March 12, 1955, Harry Klasmeier, equipped with his knowledge of fire protection and with the power and the force of the fire prevention code, bid Mrs. Frances Kennedy, his hard working secretary, good-bye, got behind the wheel of his county-owned 1955 Ford Fairlane, equipped with siren and flashing light and painted red with the Anne Arundel County Fire Prevention emblem on the door, and cruised up Ritchie Highway toward Brooklyn.[25]

After stopping by the Brooklyn Fire station to visit with either Ed Utz or Frank Homberg—one would have been working as the engineman that day—Harry finished a sandwich he had brought along and headed down to Arundel Park. He parked the Fairlane on the large lot and for a moment or two stared at the massive structure. The main hall had a massive Quonset-style roof covered with black felt paper and tar. From its size and prior inspections he had conducted on smaller buildings, he knew he would probably spend the remainder of the afternoon at Arundel Park.

The concrete block walls, eight inches thick and twelve feet high, that enclosed the milk bar, front entrance, and kitchen were painted white with metal advertising signs attached near the roof's edge. Alternating red and white panels of aluminum made up the awnings over the exterior doors. Multiple rows of linked white neon bulbs, unlit this afternoon, outlined the block walls near the roof's edge. After Harry had sized up the front of the building, he placed his keys in his pocket and put on his fire marshal's cap. He then took up his clipboard with notepad and forms, walked into the milk bar, and introduced himself to the manager.

As he had done on countless inspections in the past, Harry went back outside to conduct a 360-degree evaluation of the exterior. A walk around the entire structure let him measure the building's perimeter, locate the exits, service doors, electrical panels, gas pipes, and shutoffs. He would note the outside storage of combustibles such as cardboard or wooden boxes, the placement of its fence, the presence of high and possibly combustible weeds, and any flammable or combustible liquid stored in containers.

When he had finished with the exterior, Klasmeier took off his cap, wiped a little sweat from his brow, lit up a cigar, and sat down at a picnic table at the rear of the building. He put a fresh sheet of paper in his clipboard and drew a plan of the complex. Its dimensions would help him compute the capacity of the building, or the maximum number of people allowed for a major event. (See Appendix A.)

Continuing with his inspection inside, Klasmeier noticed that the concrete walls were painted a dark green up to the window sills. Above the sills they were painted white. A couple of men were rearranging some of the long tables and metal chairs for the evening's bingo games. Klasmeier meticulously checked the panic hardware mounted on the exit doors. Panic hardware, required in theaters, auditoriums and other buildings such as Arundel Park's where entry is controlled, allows the necessary additional exits to be closed and locked during a function or event. In an emergency, the hardware lets the door open when someone exerts approximately fifteen pounds of pressure against the metal bar that extends the length of the door leaf. The compressed bar mechanically attached to the latching and locking assembly pops the door open, permitting an unobstructed escape.

Harry also looked at the exit sign lights above the exit doors to determine if they worked. Next he examined the condition of the metal flue pipe vents attached to the ceiling-mounted gas heaters, furnace, and cooking equipment ductwork and found them all to be in a fair condition. Experience had taught him that disconnections or openings in the metal flues could result in carbon monoxide poisoning and that dirty and greasy venting equipment in the kitchen provided an excellent conduit for "fire spread" in the event of a high fire on the stovetop.

Careful not to miss anything, Harry opened the doors to storage rooms, offices, and the cloak room. His trained eyes scanned these areas from ceiling to floor and from wall to wall. He looked for trash, rags, brooms, floor mops, clothing, cardboard and paper, or other combustible materials in disarray. Harry had been taught that these conditions breed fires and encourage fire spread once a fire starts. He found all housekeeping in these enclosures to be satisfactory.

The inspection required Harry to check out the electrical cords attached to the many appliances throughout the facility. Were the cords frayed or damaged? Was any copper wiring exposed? When exposed wiring comes into contact with a metal object, the wire will overheat and can lead to a fire. Extension cords and multi-outlet plugs serving a number of appliances

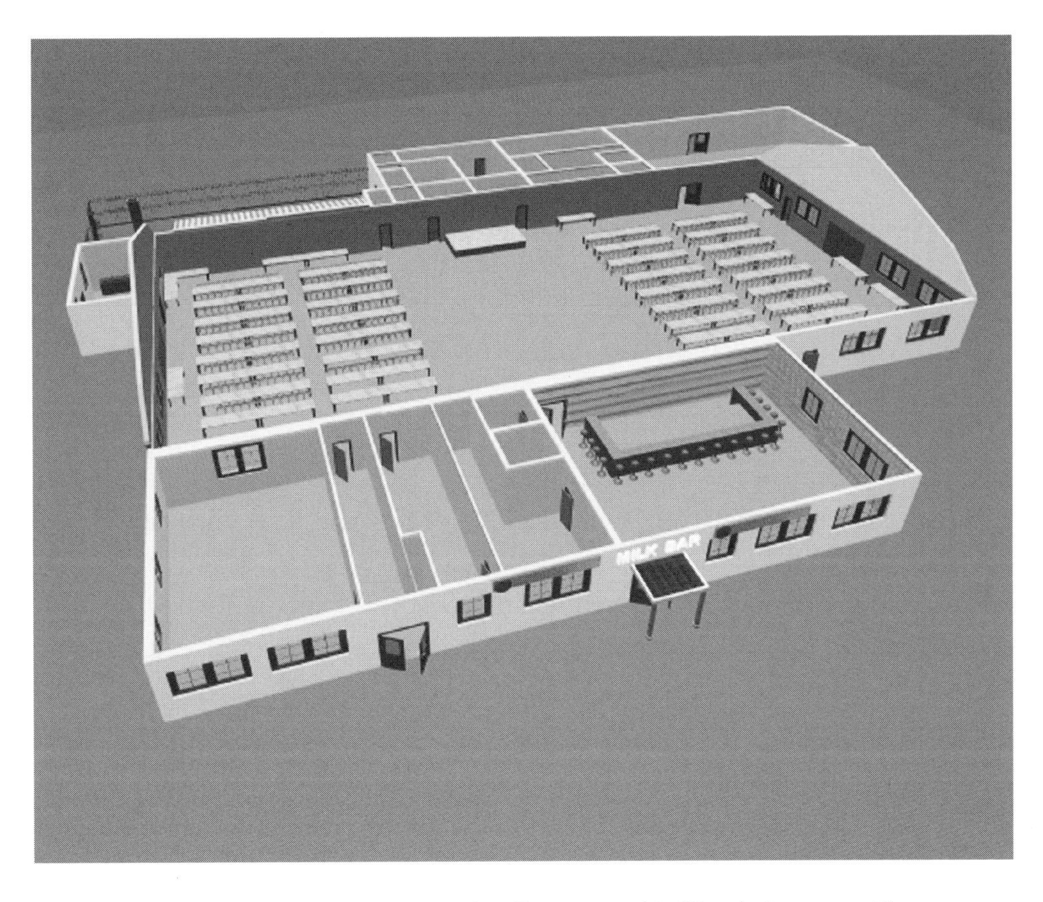

Floor layout of Arundel Park as it existed in January 1956. (Rendering created by Harry Steiner.)

might also overheat and result in fires. Harry saw no extension cords or damaged wiring during the inspection.

Arundel Park was equipped with two types of portable fire extinguishers. One type, soda and acid, when inverted extinguishes by cooling the fire with water. Mounted to the wall, the cylindrical three-foot-long polished metal container was characterized by its metal "crown" usually painted blue. With its rubber hose and plastic nozzle an operator could project a stream of water up to about twenty feet for a limited period if the extinguisher had been maintained properly and serviced once a year. (See Appendix A.)

Harry checked the small cardboard tag attached by a string to the crown on the extinguisher and noted that it had been serviced that year. The Class A rated extinguisher was only approved for small fires involving paper, cardboard, clothing, wood, trash, and other ordinary combustibles.

Five soda and acid extinguishers were mounted and unobstructed on the walls at various points.[26]

The other type of fire extinguisher was the carbon dioxide type (CO_2). With its cylindrical container made of a heavy gauged steel and painted red with a hard rubber insulated hose attached to a nozzle, it was filled with ten pounds of compressed liquid carbon dioxide that turned into a gas when released. Unlike the soda and acid extinguisher, the CO_2 did not have to be inverted. A "spray nozzle" trigger much like that of a garden hose was mounted on the top of the cylinder. An attached hard rubber hose with a cone-like nozzle directed the cold, expanding, white gas at the flames. Upon discharge, the pressurized CO_2 gas spiraling around in the plastic cone created a distinctive sound, like that of a muted fog horn, when the gas was released.

The CO_2 extinguisher smothers the fire by eliminating its oxygen. This Class BC rated extinguisher was very effective on small grease and liquid fuel fires, and fires involving energized electrical equipment. The facility had three of them, two mounted in the kitchen. Their service tags also indicated they had been checked in 1955.

On March 12, 1955, Chief Fire Marshal Harry Klasmeier found Arundel Park to be in good order as far as the fire prevention code was concerned and most likely shared this information with the facility's manager before heading back to the Annapolis office and filing his report.[27] It must be noted here that there was some controversy involving the doors leading from the arena's hall into and through the lounge. Klasmeier made a note on his report that these doors were locked during events in the hall. It is not clear whether he required corrective action be taken.

As Harry drove south through Brooklyn Park on Ritchie Highway, he noticed teenagers standing along the roadway, waiting at the school crossing at the busy intersection of Hammonds Lane. He tapped on the horn and waved to the crossing guard, an elderly gentleman, who looked much younger then his age and worked part-time as a special policeman for Anne Arundel County. Twice a day the special policeman assisted the teenagers from the nearby Brooklyn Park High School across the dangerous highway.

The crossing guard's name was Andrew Brady, a retired Baltimore City firefighter, whom Harry knew well. Brady lived only a few blocks away on Magie Street, not far from the school crossing. He also worked as an

Anne Arundel County Special Police Officer for events at Arundel Park and other facilities that held public gatherings. Brady was a highly respected and upstanding citizen, a father, husband, and grandfather. As were many others living in the Brooklyn area, Brady was as also an active member of the nearby Saint Rose of Lima Catholic Church.[28]

Saint Rose of Lima's second church, constructed in 1916 after the small wooden church burned to the ground, suffered the same fate in April 1950. (Joseph B. Ross, Jr.)

3

A Church Emerges from Ashes

In the first decades of the twentieth century, the Brooklyn community's demographics gradually changed as the original Anglo-Saxon inhabitants made room for first- and second-generation immigrants from Poland, Germany, and the Ukraine.[1] Families with names like Smith, Taubman, Helmsettler, Cromwell, and Pumphrey, were now living near and working beside new faces, with names like Sokolis, Machovec, Kozlowski, Speigle, and Rozmarynowski. Possessed of a strong work ethic and devoted to their churches, the newcomers from Eastern Europe found jobs in Brooklyn's factories, oil refineries, railroad yards, and on the wharves.

Although the 1919 annexation by the city created a new boundary line that ran straight through the heart of the Brooklyn community, the town's hard-working people remained united. The small business owners, skilled blue-collar workers, and general laborers and their spouses continued on with their daily lives. They socialized, played, and worshiped together as various little churches representing a number of different religious denominations, began to dot the Brooklyn landscape.

In 1914, as the Brooklyn Volunteer Fire Department at 5th Street and Pontiac Avenue was commemorating five years of service to the community, another viable organization was taking root only a few blocks away. The Saint Rose of Lima Catholic Church, named for the first canonized saint of the New World, celebrated its first mass in a small, newly built, one-and-a-half story wooden church on the east side of 4th Street between Washburn Avenue and Talbot Street. The land for this new mission of the Saint Athanasius Catholic Church in nearby Curtis Bay had been donated by Brooklyn's Helmsettler family.[2]

On Sunday, February 7, 1915, sometime around noon, the siren began to wail from the cupola atop the Brooklyn Fire Station. Mr. Huber's horses were hitched up to the station's hose and chemical wagon, and off they galloped into the crisp winter air to a reported fire at the new Saint Rose of Lima Church. Despite the volunteers' efforts, the fire completely destroyed it. No one ever learned how the fire started, but rumor had it that the Klu Klux Klan, which was active in the area, might have played a part in the Catholic church's destruction.[3]

Construction immediately began on a second, much larger church on the site, this one built of brick. It was dedicated on February 6, 1916, and during the next few years the parish membership grew until it included worshipers from other areas of the city and county. The growing complex of church structures eventually spanned Talbot Street and continued one block to Jeffrey Street. In 1922, Father Leonard J. Ripple succeeded Father F. L. Kunnecke as the parish's second pastor. Father Ripple's reign, overseeing the greatest expansion of the church and school, would continue almost four decades until his passing in 1961.

Twelve years after the fire in the first wooden church, as the parish was preparing for the forthcoming Christmas celebration, tragedy struck again, this time testing the Baltimore City Fire Department crew at 5th and Pontiac. At 1:23 A.M. on the bitter cold morning of December 21, 1926, the alarm sounded. The new parish school, in operation for only six months, was on fire.[4] The new career crew did not fare much better than the volunteers had a dozen years before. Three alarms brought nineteen pieces of fire apparatus from across Baltimore City, but many of the responding units were delayed for up to half an hour by a freight train that blocked the Hanover/Light Street railroad crossing.[5]

That delay, and insufficient available water, allowed the fire to grow beyond the capabilities of the Brooklyn crew. The new three-story masonry school building was completely destroyed. As before, fire would not hinder the growing parish. A new and larger school opened in the fall of 1927.[6]

Saint Rose of Lima flourished and provided for more than the community's spiritual needs. Programs were developed to assist the poor, the sick, and the disadvantaged. The church supported the work of the Dominican Sisters and other Catholic associated organizations such as the Knights of Columbus. Through the efforts of Father Ripple's administration, missions were established that resulted in today's Saint Jane Francis in Rivera Beach and Holy Trinity in Glen Burnie.

In 1950, Saint Rose of Lima received a new family into the church. Andrew Brady, his wife Edith, sons Andrew Jr. and John, and daughters Nancy and Betty moved from their home three miles away from the church, on Riverside Avenue in Baltimore's Locust Point, to Magie Street in Brooklyn Park. At the time, Magie Street between Walton Avenue and Church Street was a dirt road. Andrew and son John, whom everyone called Bill, bought building lots on the east side of the street and contracted with Brooklyn Park builder Henry Boyne for two one-story "Greenwood" style houses. The two Brady households would live side by side and share a common driveway.[7]

Andrew Brady had spent most of his life in public service, putting in more than twenty years with the Baltimore City Fire Department. He'd seen his first service as a firefighter assigned to Truck 19, located with Engine 17 at the fire station on the corner of Haubert Street and Fort Avenue in January 1921. Brady worked throughout South Baltimore during his career, and also served for a time with the elite and tightly knit Rescue 1 unit in the station at Paca and Mulberry Streets from 1926 to 1928.

Bill Brady has fond memories of his dad driving Engine 17, the big open-cab Ahrens Fox fire pumper, up and down Fort Avenue in the 1930s, responding to fires in Locust Point and elsewhere in the city. As Bill walked to and from school or played with friends, he remembers waving to his dad and his father waving back as the big rig with its ancient solid rubber tires rumbled along the brick streets of Locust Point.[8]

Prior to his retirement in 1943, Andrew Brady had been promoted to assistant engineman and operated the pumper assigned to Engine 26 at the station on West Street. He played for the department football team between 1930 and 1933 and participated in the annual games between the firefighters and U.S. Marines stationed in Quantico, Virginia.[9]

Although Bill lived right next door, Andrew spent most of his time with his oldest son Andrew Jr. The two were inseparable. They painted houses together, upholstered cars and furniture, and worked as stevedores on Baltimore's busy waterfront.

Stevedoring paid great money, providing the ships were in to load or unload. But it was not steady work. As a result, Andrew Jr. took on a more secure position as a patrolman with the Anne Arundel County Police Department and was assigned to the Northern District in nearby Ferndale. Bill, two years younger than his brother, would eventually wind up back in Locust Point as an employee with the Coca Cola Company, working in an impressive looking two-story brick building on Fort Avenue.[10]

The Bradys were a tightly knit group. Daughter Nancy later married John Thompson, an employee with the Baltimore Gas and Electric Company, and moved two houses down from brother Bill on the corner of Magie Street and Walton Avenue. Betty married and bought a house on Gischel Street directly behind her father's. (Years later even most of the grandchildren would buy houses on or around Magie Street.) Less than a mile from Magie Street, Andrew Brady's nephew, George Feeley, lived on Doris Avenue off Ritchie Highway. George, encouraged by his Uncle Andrew, was the only member of the family to follow in his uncle's footsteps and join the Baltimore City Fire Department.

In the early 1950s, Andrew Jr. found employment for his father as a special police officer for Anne Arundel County. Special police were part-time peace officers who worked traffic, school crossings and events such as oyster and bull roasts, bingo games, carnivals, and other large community gatherings. Although they wore a full uniform, badge, and cap, and carried a gun, it is not clear that in the 1950s special police officers had the power to arrest.[11]

Andrew Brady's new job kept him busy, and with his volunteering at the church he spent many weekends away from Magie Street. All the Bradys along with cousin George Feeley volunteered for church and school activities for Saint Rose of Lima.

The church had survived two major fires, the Depression, and two world wars. It looked as if the tragedy and destruction that had marked the church's early years were now behind this prospering parish, which now numbered more than six thousand.[12]

Then, on the evening of April 22, 1950, an altar boy by the name of

James Parks was walking to the rectory when he noticed flames flickering through the main building's stained glass windows. On opening a door to the church and seeing smoke, he ran to the rectory to have someone notify the fire department. The Baltimore City Fire Department received the report at 7:15 P.M., and responding firefighters could see the smoke and flames from several blocks away. The fire seemed to have started and created the most damage in the 4th Street and Washburn Avenue section near the front entrance.[13]

Hundreds of stricken townspeople and parishioners looked on in despair as the two alarms of personnel and equipment worked for thirty minutes to bring the fire under control. Brooklyn's 35 Engine and crew laid a supply hose in the street from a fire hydrant and dragged the attack hose line through a doorway near the rectory to fight the fire near the altar. Engine 57 of Curtis Bay, the second company to arrive, stretched an additional attack hose line through the main entrance of the church and up the stairway. From there they stopped the fire at the ceiling over the choir loft and prevented it from completely burning down the building.

But because the fire had destroyed the roof and water damage was severe throughout the structure, the building had to be completely razed. That was done in July, and construction on a new building begun. When it was completed the new church, designed in a colonial American architectural style and trimmed in limestone, presented an impressive sight. The building was dedicated on November 23, 1952.[14]

After the April 22 fire, father Ripple was interviewed by the newspapers. He believed the fire started because someone had been careless with a lighted candle, or "vigil light," and added that a similar fire had occurred over twenty years ago as a result "of children carelessly lighting devotional candles." On that occasion, Father Ripple had put out the fire himself with a portable fire extinguisher.[15]

In the final days of December 1955, Monsignor Ripple was elated with his accomplishments at Saint Rose of Lima. Although the church had suffered two devastating fires during his reign, no one had been hurt, and no life lost. With more than four thousand members listed on its rolls, even after the establishment of Saint Francis and Holy Trinity, the parish was still growing and expanding. Nineteen fifty-five had been a prosperous year, and 1956 promised to be even better, for in the plans was a modern three-story school. Construction was scheduled to begin within the year. With more than 750 children, the current brick and wooden building was aging and overcrowded. Additionally, the entire parish was looking forward to Monsignor Ripple's "Golden Jubilee" of ordination. A celebration would be held on June 21, 1956. Yes, 1956 looked to be the best year yet.[16]

The Holy Name Society is a religious fellowship organization made up of Catholic men. Each parish sponsors a group within the society whose mission is to "beget due love and reverence for the Holy Name of God and Jesus Christ." The society supports and undertakes a number of charitable and spiritual activities, such as providing food and clothing to the community's poor, visiting the sick and infirmed, providing assistance to families who have experienced a death or serious illness, and providing religious education to people residing in the community. In order to generate the necessary revenue to support its efforts, the society sponsored fundraisers. In November and December of 1955, plans were in place and tickets were being sold for a fundraising oyster roast to be held at Arundel Park at 4901 Belle Grove Road from 1:00 to 6:00 P.M. on Sunday, January 29, 1956.

On Friday, the twenty-seventh, late in the afternoon, Roy Helms sat down in the kitchen of his flagstone-covered Cape Cod at the corner of Ritchie Highway and 14th Avenue. Roy, who worked sixteen-hour days most weeks at the prosperous Arundel Park, needed a night off. He picked up a copy of the *Baltimore News-Post* and sipped a hot cup of instant coffee. After briefly scanning the news of the day, he checked the weather section.[17] The National Weather Bureau's Baltimore office predicted rain or snow for Sunday. "Bad weather," he thought to himself, "Glad I had Elmer put up those extra coat racks in the cloak room. . . . We're surely going to need them."[18]

"Sunday," he mused. It was hard to believe. Roy had kept so busy since his wife Annie had passed away less than three years before, he had almost forgotten. He tried very hard not to think about it, but his heart already felt the familiar ache. How could he forget?

He decided to go back down to the park facility and help Bob plan for Sunday's activities. Work would ease his mind. Annie would have been fifty-seven years old on Sunday, January 29, her birthday.[19]

MARYLAND'S FINEST—CA$H PRIZE$

BINGO

— AT —

ARUNDEL PARK

4901 Belle Grove Rd. Brooklyn Park PRospect 0947

8:30 P. M.

EACH **TUES. - FRI. - SAT.** NITE

FREE BUSES TO AND FROM

At ARUNDEL PARK each ball is televised when called, likewise each winning card is televised when called back for verification. This is your protection against human errors. Now in addition to the Regular $50.00 Prizes you will play for TWO ADDITIONAL JACKPOTS at "NO" ADDITIONAL COST TO YOU. Other Jackpot Games with Prizes EQUALLED BY NONE. Cash Door Prizes.

THE ARUNDEL PARK RESTAURANT

Open 7 Days A Week

FOR FASTER CARRY OUT SERVICE CALL PROSPECT 0947

SPECIALS FOR:

WED. 25th	— Fresh Ham & Sour Kraut	.75
THURS. 26th	— Roast Lamb	.75
FRI. 27th	— Steak Fish	.75
SAT. 28th	— Creamed Chicken On Toast	.75
SUN. 29th	— Roast Beef Dinner	.95
MON. 30th	— Fried Chicken Leg	.75
TUES. 31st	— Meat Loaf	.75

OYSTER ROAST

SUNDAY, JANUARY 29, 1956

1—6 P.M.

Sponsored by

ST. ROSE OF LIMA HOLY NAME SOCIETY

Plenty Of Delicious Food and Drink For All

Dancing - - - Admission $3.00 Per Person

BALTIMORE POLICE POST No. 1539 V.F.W.

OYSTER ROAST

Sunday, February 12, 1956

*Last advertisement for Arundel Park. Note the "Oyster Roast" announcement in the lower section. (*Brooklyn News, *January 25, 1956.)*

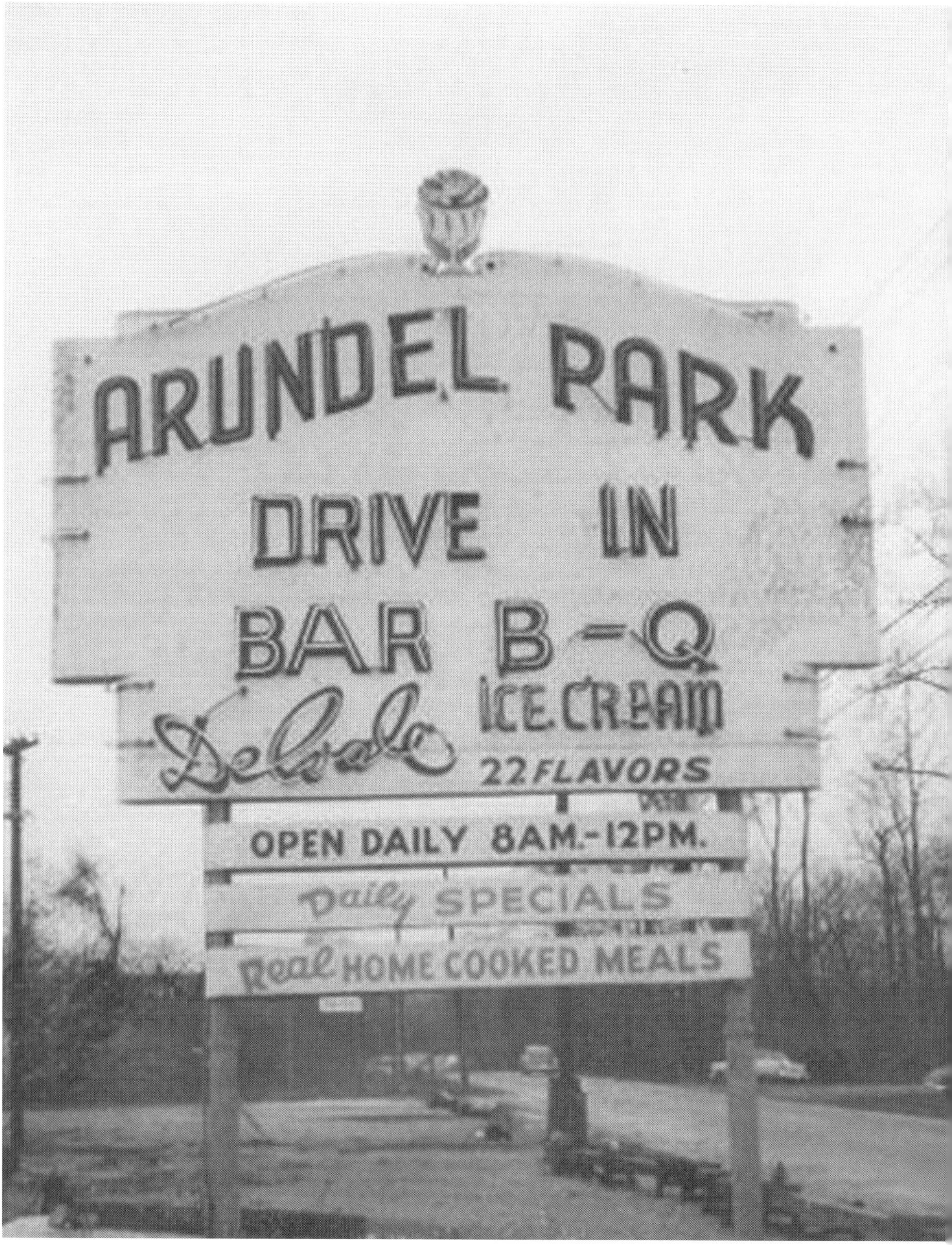

ARUNDEL PARK
DRIVE IN
BAR B-Q
ICE CREAM
22 FLAVORS
OPEN DAILY 8AM.-12PM.
Daily SPECIALS
Real HOME COOKED MEALS

4

Oysters, Beer, and Games of Chance

January 29, 1956, began as just another cold, winter Sunday in Brooklyn. Bells pealed, as the churches called their congregations to celebrate mass and attend services. Thousands of families were soon walking or driving to church and Sunday school. The congregation at Saint Rose had grown so large that three masses were held at different times on Sunday morning. For each mass there were two services held simultaneously, one in the main area of the first floor, and one in the basement chapel.

In all denominations, a segment of the mass or service is reserved for announcements that inform the parishioners of church-sponsored events. At Saint Rose no doubt one of the announcements that morning concerned an oyster roast sponsored by the Holy Name Society to be held later that day at Arundel Park. Although busy with the morning masses, Father Zukowski, Father Wills, and Father Murphy all looked forward to attending. Father Austin Murphy would succeed Father Ripple as the church's monsignor in the 1960s and would later become a bishop.[1]

Because the state's blue laws barred retail sales on Sundays, the new Food Fair store located on the northbound lane of Ritchie Highway was closed. Packed with busy shoppers only the day before, the store was now dark and quiet, and the parking lot was empty. But across the highway the older Sanitary Food Market was open. Located between 10th and 11th

Engineman Eddie Utz outside the front of the station with mascot "Smoky," circa 1955. (Charlie Doegen and Les Helfrich.)

Avenues, the Sanitary, open twenty-four hours a day, had been established before the blue laws went into effect. Anyone looking south a block from the Sanitary Food Market to the corner of 11th Avenue would have noticed activity in front of the Brooklyn Fire Station.

As a light drizzle began to fall, Brooklyn Volunteer Fire Department engineman Eddie Utz decided to back the station's fleet into the building before the equipment became wet. As he was backing the last vehicle, the big, shiny, red Mack fire pumper truck, into the station, he paid close attention to the mirrors on both the sides of the open cab, because the doorways for the apparatus were narrow and the engine bays were not well-lighted. He didn't want to hit anything.

With the engine backed inside the warm and dry two-story fire station, Ed wiped off the vehicles and checked out the equipment. The water tanks of both main engines had been filled. The fire extinguishers, the tool boxes, first-aid kits, axes, nozzles, hose, hose couplings and fittings were in order. He inspected all the apparatus, including the ambulance, for proper levels of engine oil and cooling water, and possible leaks in hose connections. He checked the tire pressure and wheel lugs. He operated the pumps and checked the chromed-lined, glass-covered instrument gauges on the operator's panel to make sure the huge engines were ready for action. When he had finished,

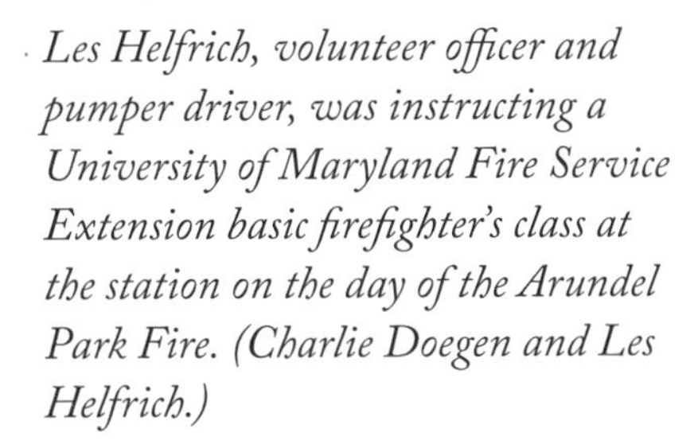

Les Helfrich, volunteer officer and pumper driver, was instructing a University of Maryland Fire Service Extension basic firefighter's class at the station on the day of the Arundel Park Fire. (Charlie Doegen and Les Helfrich.)

Ed recorded his activities into the station log book in the small alarm/radio room on the first floor of the station.

In the station's little kitchen, he sat down at the table, poured a cup of coffee, picked up the Sunday papers and began reading the front page news. A possible Baltimore Transit Company strike threatened to shut down Baltimore City the following morning. If the strike was called, the greater Baltimore Metropolitan area of one and a half million people would be left without public transportation.[2]

Les Helfrich came in, gave Ed a quick hello, and ran up the steps to the second floor. Les was there to conduct the University of Maryland's Fire Service Extension Department's basic firefighting class.[3]

Today would complete the second eight-hour segment of the forty-hour program. Fire Service Extension training was typically held on weekday evenings and weekends to accommodate those in the volunteer force who attended high school or worked full-time jobs during the week. The program offered a structured set of classes in fire department organization, protective gear, hose line and fire stream handling, nozzles, air masks, ladders, forcible entry, debris overhaul, and salvage. It also provided a rare opportunity to fight a real live fire in the Extension Department's training fire building at the campus in College Park.[4]

As Les made last-minute preparations in the makeshift classroom set up in the station's second floor all purpose hall, he wondered how he was going to pull this off by himself. The program's backup instructor, Frank Homberg, the engineman and deputy chief who sometimes referred to himself as an "old fire horse," was across the street in his 11th Avenue house, sick in bed. The old fire horse had come down with the flu.[5]

Les would have to do it alone today. Since it was a small class, he thought he could manage. Les pushed his long, thin blonde hair back across the top of his head, wiped his wire-rimmed glasses with a handkerchief, and looked around the room one more time to make sure all the tables, chairs, visual aids, and equipment were in their proper places. Moments later the young men from the Brooklyn, Rivera Beach, and Lake Shore departments began to arrive and take their seats.[6] Most of the volunteers who showed up that morning would never forget this class or this day.

Approximately half a mile west of the fire station, workers were busy in Arundel Park's kitchen, near the back of the building, getting ready for the event. Since 8:00 a.m., church members along with workers from the park had been busy unloading bushel baskets of oysters to be steamed and fried. The large overhead garage door on the east end of the building was open. Boxes of containers filled with ketchup, mustard, mayonnaise, "Old Bay" seasoning, horseradish, potato chips, and pretzels, along with paper plates, plastic cups, napkins, and eating utensils were lugged into the hall.[7] Kegs of beer were hauled to a couple of small, temporary refreshment bars along the walls in the main hall. There they would be set in metal half-barrels filled with ice, ready when the first attendees arrived at 1:00 p.m.[8]

Women of the church, some of whom had worked at the hall for eight hours the day before, were busy in the kitchen making their own final preparations.[9] There would be potato and macaroni salads, cole slaw, mashed potatoes, roast beef and gravy, cold cuts, cheese, lettuce and tomatoes, raw oysters, steamed oysters, and fried oyster fritters. Living near the Chesapeake Bay had its culinary advantages.

Workers from Arundel Park were setting up large "money wheels" behind tables whose tops had been marked with numbers. The wheel itself, with corresponding numbers on its rim, was attached to a partition behind the crews working the tables. Patrons put money down roulette-fashion on

Taken in 1954 or 1955, this is the only existing photograph of the interior of Arundel Park. The tables and chairs are set up for Bingo night. The large overhead door in the background, is at the west end of the building. Both would figure prominently on the afternoon of January 29, 1956, as would the four-by-eight-foot ceiling panels. (Courtesy of the Hearst Corporation.)

the table numbers as the wheel was spun. The prize might be a cake, a stuffed animal, a potted plant, or cash. The money wheels were set up near the walls along with a number of "one-armed bandits"—slot machines.[10]

Baltimore's proximity to the Chesapeake Bay makes oyster roasts indigenous to the region. Saint Rose of Lima's was just one of many oyster roasts being held on this Sunday. The Saint Mark's Men's Club was holding a roast at the Dixie Ballroom at Gwynn Oak Park in West Baltimore.

One was about to get under way downtown in Saint Andrew's Hall at Monument and Washington Streets. The Calvert Hall Alumni Association was sponsoring still another at the Aisquith Pleasure Club. All charged $3.00 per person except the "Dixie" Ballroom, which charged $3.50.[11]

Driving his 1954 Chevrolet down the 5th Avenue hill, Frank Kvech Jr., a bus driver for the Baltimore Transit Company, stopped at the stop sign at Belle Grove Road. As Frank turned left onto Belle Grove Road en route to the Arundel Park, he was thinking about the Saint Rose of Lima oyster roasts he had helped with over the years. There were so many he stopped counting.

Frank had volunteered his time again today, but the roast was not the only thing on his mind. Negotiations, between the Baltimore Transit Bus Company and the union over raising the $1.90 hourly wage to $2.00 and reducing the length of the work week had broken down on Friday. So far this weekend nothing had been accomplished, and talks had reached a stalemate. It looked like tomorrow morning the union would walk out and strike. Like hundreds of the city's hard-working bus and trolley drivers, Frank didn't know what he was going to do. A strike in 1952 had lasted three weeks. (This one would last for over a month.)[12]

About a mile and a half east of the Arundel Park complex, eighteen-year-old Louise Sokolis was in her second-floor bedroom in her parents' rowhouse on 4th Street in Brooklyn's Arundel Village, not far from busy Church Street, which links Brooklyn Park with Curtis Bay. Lou, as most people called her, was concentrating on the finishing touches of her makeup. She had finally found the perfect dress and was learning how to walk in her new high-heeled shoes. Having attended mass that morning at Saint Rose of Lima Catholic Church, about a mile away, Lou was joyfully looking forward to her first oyster roast.

But there was a problem. Though she was still seeing her old boyfriend, she had just started dating another boy whom she really liked. Lou could not make up her mind. She didn't want either of them to know that she was going to the oyster roast, and the thing she feared most was that both would show up and possibly get into a fight. As she brushed her long, pretty auburn hair, she contemplated the little white lies she would use so they wouldn't find out. Lou just wanted to have a day out to dance, to have fun, and enjoy the company of her girlfriends.

Around 11:00 A.M., over on Magie Street, Andrew Brady put on his special police officer's blue uniform. As he stood before the bathroom mirror combing his hair, he thought about a decision and a promise he had made, one that his wife had greatly encouraged. Recently, Brady had been working more hours then he wanted to and had promised Edith that today's Arundel Park assignment would be his last event. From now on, Brady would only work the school crossing duty during the week.[13]

A little later, as Brady was backing his big blue Plymouth out of the driveway that separated his house from his son's, Bill, always the prankster, remembers walking behind the car and misdirecting his father with hand signals until his father was driving on the grass. That led to more father-son bantering.

Bill himself had other plans for this Sunday. He was getting ready to take his wife and kids to the movies. (The Pennington in Curtis Bay was showing a double feature: *The Tender Trap,* starring Frank Sinatra, and *The Gun that Won the West,* starring Dennis Morgan. Doors opened at 1:30.) Originally he had wanted to attend the oyster roast because over the years he had enjoyed any number of functions at Arundel Park, but last weekend something had happened that would put a temporary, perhaps even a permanent halt to any plans for fun down there.[14] The previous Sunday, Bill had been sitting at one of Arundel Park's long, portable, wooden tables eating a roast beef sandwich and drinking a beer when he noticed a problem developing between a number of inebriated patrons and his father, who was working the event as a special police officer. Bill then saw his older brother Andrew Jr. step in. The agitated group and the two Bradys went outside. Bill put down his beer and sandwich and followed. In the parking lot, the fight was already in progress. His father was fighting three and his brother two others. Bill joined the ruckus, and a few minutes later Andrew Jr. flashed his county police officer's badge and threatened the thugs with arrest. They all fled.[15]

One consequence of the brawl in the parking lot was that Bill's wife forbade him to attend this Sunday's oyster roast and insisted he spend the afternoon with the family. The fight had also contributed to the elder Andrew Brady's decision to stop working at Arundel Park. At nearly six feet and 230 pounds, the big Irishman was good with his fists and had always been able to take care of himself, but at fifty-seven, enough was enough.

As the senior Brady backed out of the driveway and drove up Magie Street toward Church Street, it was the last time Bill would ever see his father well.[16]

By 2:00 P.M., Arundel Park was packed. The fundraiser had been oversold, and there were more people than seats. Some complained and got their money back. They left angry and grumbling.[17]

The many who stayed chatted and socialized. Small groups of men discussed whether or not the young Baltimore Orioles would be any match for the World Series Champion Brooklyn Dodgers in the event the "Birds" won the American League pennant. They discussed cars and whether the price of gas would rise to an unheard-of twenty-five cents a gallon.[18] Women gossiped and complained about the quality of the food and wondered how it was possible that a handsome movie actor named James Dean could die in an automobile accident at such a young age.

The band played contemporary standards. On the open floor in the middle of the hall, couples danced. Some embraced, while others stood in front of the bandstand, watching the musicians. Over the music and the hundreds of loud conversations, one could hear the occasional excited shout as someone won a prize at the money wheels or hit the "one-armed bandits" for a payout. Light smoke rolling in through the open door carried the smell of burning wood from the fires steaming the oysters. The crowd was enjoying themselves.[19]

Twenty-year-old Frank Kvech III truly loved oyster roasts. He was looking forward to a good time before going back to work in the warehouse of Lord Baltimore Candy and Tobacco Company on Monday morning. Frank still boasts of the Saint Rose of Lima oyster roasts during those years. They were known for the inexhaustible quantity of good food. Tickets were nearly always sold out.[20]

Frank III remembers attending oyster roasts as a kid. Many were held in the third-floor auditorium of the Saint Rose of Lima Church School on 4th Street where he was enrolled. He has fond memories of the stage being used for food preparation and of his dad, Frank Jr., cooking. On this day, his father was also one of about two hundred volunteers from the church working the event. They prepared food, served tables, poured beer and soda, helped with the money wheels, sold raffle tickets, and cleaned up used paper plates and empty paper cups.

Around 3:00 P.M. the younger Frank remembers being outside on the east side of the building with his buddy, an electrician. The weather had turned into a light drizzle, and they could hear a noticeable buzzing coming from the neon lights along the roof line. His buddy told him he would like to come back during the week to see if he could make some money repairing the circuitry.

The festivities continued throughout the afternoon. Twelve hundred people ate, drank, danced, talked, gambled, and generally had a good time.[21] A number of couples who could not find babysitters had brought their children along.

As Special Police Officer Andrew Brady walked around, helping out where he could and patrolling the hall for disturbances, his nephew George Feeley tended one of the portable bars set up near the east side overhead door. George, now assigned as a firefighter with Engine 35 at the 5th Street station in Brooklyn, was volunteering his time this Sunday at the affair for the church.[22]

Other customers were being served at the milk bar in the front of the building, as well as in the attached "Helms Park Cocktail Lounge" on the other side near the southwest corner. To keep nonpaying customers from entering the oyster roast, the doorways from the main hall through the milk bar and lounge were locked.[23]

5

Fatal Delay

As dusk settled on the Arundel Park complex, those traveling up and down the two-lane Belle Grove Road may have remarked on all the cars packed into the large lot, many parked in double rows right up to and against the building. Passers-by might even have noticed smoke. Yet, because of the melting snow that had covered Brooklyn earlier in the week and the cooking going on outside behind the main building, patches of fog and smoke were to be expected. Besides, Arundel Park workers were always burning something in the fenced-in area behind the kitchen, so smoke hovering around the building was not unusual.[1]

About 4:55 P.M., an hour and five minutes before the event was scheduled to shut down, men working the outside stoves saw black smoke emanating from a cornice between the concrete block wall and the wooden roof of the kitchen.[2] Charles Johnson of Brooklyn, who was standing near the raw bar, grabbed a small garden hose near the oyster steamer and climbed onto the rear deck of a pickup truck belonging to John Secoura, who had just dropped off two barrels of oysters. Secoura's truck was parked very close to the kitchen, and from there Johnson played a stream of water on the fire.[3]

From his vantage point Johnson could look into the hole in the wood created by the fire and see that much of the concealed space between the ceiling and the roof above the kitchen was involved. At almost the same moment that Johnson climbed onto Secoura's truck, those inside the kitchen discovered fire in the ceiling in the same general area. No one thought it necessary to call the fire department.[4]

Walt Zylka, of Brooklyn, who had joined those attempting to suppress the fire outside, heard the commotion in the kitchen. He went inside and with a carbon dioxide fire extinguisher quickly knocked down the flames penetrating from the ceiling. When he looked up into the ceiling, he could see a fire glow moving toward the main hall.[5] Still, no one called the fire department or began an evacuation of the building.

Delay of alarm is not uncommon. Those confronted with fire often make an attempt to extinguish it themselves. Sometimes they are successful; many times they are not and waste precious minutes that would have been better spent alerting occupants and notifying the fire department.

In 1958 a deadly fire climbed a stairway undetected and penetrated the second-floor hallway of the Our Lady of Angels Catholic School in Chicago, trapping more than 250 children. Time passed, and no one called the fire department. Passers-by, seeing flames and smoke pouring from the structure, reacted with confusion, disbelief, and indecision. Not only did they delay in contacting the fire department, no one notified the school's occupants.[6] Anywhere from eight to fifteen minutes elapsed before someone contacted the fire department, and ninety-two children and three nuns perished in the blaze. Had firefighters been called five minutes sooner, most of those children would have survived.[7]

Similarly, on May 28, 1977, in the infamous "Cabaret Room" at the Beverly Hills Super Club in Southgate, Kentucky, approximately twenty minutes went by after a fire was detected before patrons were notified. One hundred and sixty-five people lost their lives in the fast moving blaze.[8]

At Arundel Park on this Sunday evening, delay was once more at hand. Moreover, since the hall contained no manual fire alarm, automatic fire protection, or detection systems, all of which are required in today's larger places of public assembly, all critical communications had to be conveyed through word of mouth.

Approximately five minutes had elapsed since the fire was first spotted burning in the exterior cornice between the wall and the roof. No one had yet contacted the fire department or notified the occupants. Perhaps enhanced by a five-mile-per-hour wind from the southeast, the fire in the kitchen ceiling slowly worked its way upward and outward.[9] It moved unseen above the kitchen ceiling through a utility opening about a foot square in the wall separating the kitchen from the main hall. Searching for

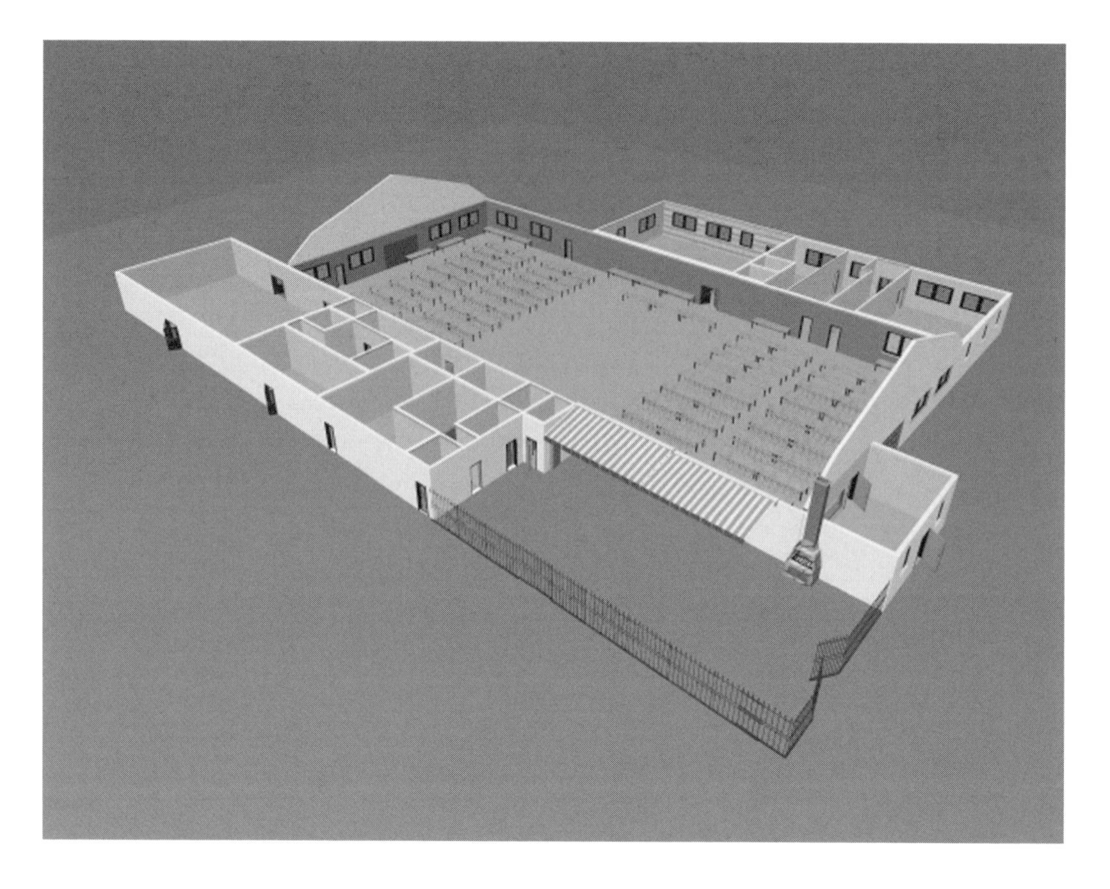

A computer rendering of the building's east side exterior. Since Arundel Park workers were always burning something in the fenced-in area behind the hall's kitchen, smoke hovering around the building was not an uncommon sight. (Harry Steiner.)

oxygen and combustible material the fire divided and multiplied in the large concealed space over the main assembly hall.[10] Beneath it, 1,200 people were completely unaware of what was developing overhead.

James Babicky, chief cook for the night, closed the door between the kitchen and the hall to reduce the fire's spread and told Leonard Anderson to notify Roy Helms, who was working in his office at the front of the building adjacent to the milk bar.[11]

Helms immediately went to the southeast corner of the hall. He could see smoke coming from around the vent pipe attached to the ceiling-mounted, gas-fired heater. Climbing onto one of the tables, Helms shut off the gas supply to the unit.[12] Still, no one called the fire department.

Pulling out a ladder that was permanently mounted to the wall, Helms climbed to the top and opened a trap door in the ceiling near the heating unit to investigate. Seeing a red, smoldering fire throughout the enclosed space, he quickly closed the trap door, came back down the ladder, and told one of his assistants: "Go tell Bob [Middlekauff] to call the fire department."[13] According to the *Baltimore News-Post,* an announcement was made from the microphone at the bandstand that "there was a slight fire caused by a short circuit, [but nobody was told to leave] and the band continued to play."[14] This announcement, if indeed it was made, went unmentioned in the official reports.

Frank Kvech III and his friend watched as the men worked around the ceiling trap door. Deciding to grab a beer before management shut down the event, the pair went to the bar near the large overhead door on the east side of the hall.[15] Nearby, in front of the bandstand, which was in the center of the hall along the south wall, Lou Sokolis and her girlfriends continued to watch the band.

Outside along Belle Grove Road, a couple of cars pulled into the crowded Arundel Park parking lot. A few people stopped to buy a burger or a milk shake at the milk bar or visit the lounge for a cold beer. They surely would have heard the band as they approached the hall. Otherwise it was peaceful outside in the fading afternoon light.

A much different atmosphere was developing inside, as observant and curious individuals and small groups began to notice the tense activity around the smoking trap door.[16] Smoke was puffing around the vent pipe of the ceiling heater. Others saw smoke issuing from the ceiling where it attached to the wall between the hall and the kitchen. Although some decided to leave, no one became particularly excited. The festivities continued.

William Walterhoefer and his wife took advantage of this small window of opportunity. Concerned about the hurried activities around the trap door, they made their way toward one of the available exits.[17]

Charles Ecker, an off-duty Baltimore City firefighter assigned to Ladder Truck 28 in Fairfield, watched Roy Helms climb back down the ladder. Ecker then picked up a carbon dioxide extinguisher. As he started up the ladder with it, Anna Brandt and her daughter watched with mounting alarm. Anna Brandt was attending her first oyster roast and celebrating her sixtieth birthday.[18]

Anna turned to her daughter Mary and said, "Let's get out of here."

Others were leaving too. Some of the anxious and worried were laughed at by those who were less concerned or too filled with drink to worry. A few of the uneasy stopped by the cloakroom on the way out to retrieve their coats.[19]

Special Police Officer Andrew Brady pulled a table close to the kitchen wall, stood on it, and attacked a small fire visible in the ceiling and wall with a fire extinguisher. As he discharged extinguishing agent at the fire, a small piece of ceiling tile dropped to the floor.[20]

Charles Ecker climbed the ladder and opened the ceiling trapdoor. A great, flashing fireball surged out, burning his head and knocking him off the ladder. Simultaneously, someone opened the large overhead door nearby on the east side of the hall to rid that area of smoke.[21]

Having smoldered, possibly for hours, quietly and undetected up above in the large, combustible attic space between the roof and the ceiling, the fire at that moment received what it had been waiting for. Fueled by the rush of fresh oxygen from the opened overhead door, the opening of the trap door, and the falling ceiling tile, the fire lashed out from its lair, racing through and across the combustible fiberboard ceiling. In an instant it had become unstoppable.

According to a newspaper article, James and Elizabeth Dulaney of Baltimore were seated at a table with Frances Obzut, Obzut's daughter Frances Cooke, and Elizabeth's sister Stella Kozlowski. When they first saw the smoke, they said, the crowd appeared to be calm, but they decided to get up and leave anyway. As the Dulaney party headed for the exit, the flames burst from the ceiling, and the crowd panicked.

It is believed that Frances Cooke turned back to assist her aging mother, Frances Obzut, who was being swept away by the "panicky mob." Elizabeth Dulaney said that the last time she saw Frances Cooke and her sister Stella Kozlowski, they had turned back to help Frances Obzut.[22]

6

Fire, Panic, and Escape

As the Dulaneys were making their way outside into the fresh air, Charles Ecker picked himself up off the floor, grabbed the extinguisher, and again climbed the ladder to the trap door. He attacked the flames roaring out of the ceiling until the cylinder was completely empty. Then, burned severely on his hands, arms, and upper body, he climbed down and tried to speed the evacuation of the building.[1]

Frank Kvech III, who was standing near the bar with his friend, was pushed out the opening of the large overhead door on the east wall by the surging crowd. He recalls no panic, screaming, or shouting, only a strong urge to move from the building.[2] George Feeley, who was tending bar at the same spot, experienced the same crowd reaction as he too was pushed out the door. Once outside, George scrambled to the windows to help those trying to climb out.[3]

Approximately forty seconds had passed since Roy Helms had opened the trap door. Large bright balls of orange and red flame burst through the ceiling in the southeast corner of the main hall.[4] Most of the people still in the building were caught completely off guard.

As William Walterhoefer and his wife were almost through the exit door, all hell broke loose.[5] People screamed and rushed toward the exits. Folding tables, metal chairs, and glass pitchers filled with beer and soda crashed to the floor. The fire now billowed across the east and south wall ceiling with the intensity of a raging wildfire.[6] Deadly smoke pierced the lungs of people who moments earlier had been dancing in the arms of loved ones to the popular "Tea for Two."[7]

During this frenzy, parents searched for their children, spouses searched for one another, many searched for relatives and friends.[8] As Lou Sokolis was making her way from the dance floor through the maze of tables and chairs, many now overturned, three or four men ran into her and knocked her into one of the tables. She fell into the tangled furniture. Lying there in the debris, aching with pain in her neck and upper back, she lost sight of her friends.

She wasn't alone. A number of people, mostly women, were pushed to the floor; some were even trampled. Twenty-four-year-old Thomas Janaskie, a machine operator for Bethlehem Steel at Baltimore's Sparrows Point plant, saw several women knocked to the floor. Once he got his girlfriend out the door, he and a friend went back inside and helped more than thirty women reach the exits.

A few minutes later, before he again went outside, Janaskie noticed another woman lying in a corner who appeared to be unconscious. Placing a handkerchief over his face and pulling a coat over his head, he attempted to pull the woman to the fresh and cool air just outside the door, but the flames forced him back before he could bring her out.[9]

As pandemonium grew inside the hall, families and friends became separated. In the mad rush for the exits, Mary lost sight of her mother, Anna Brandt. Albert Evans of Brooklyn, who had held his wife, Arbutus, by the arm in the initial scramble to the exits, lost his grip and both were knocked to the floor. He got back up and managed to get out of the building. He would find her later at one of the hospitals.[10]

Liston Kelly, a former Baltimore City policeman, was not so lucky. He lifted his young wife Theresa up to one of the high windows. Theresa was a pretty, twenty-eight-year-old first grade teacher in Anne Arundel County.[11] The mob tore her out of his grasp, and in the smoke they became separated. Kelly would never see her again.

As Doris Gorrick tried to get out of the building she heard the siren wailing on top of the Brooklyn Park Fire Station half a mile away and realized that the firefighters were now alerted to this nightmare.[12] She had lived in Brooklyn Park for years and had heard that siren hundreds of times, but now it was wailing for her and the hundreds of others trapped in what seemed like a burning "box of egg crates" that was disintegrating by the second.[13]

Others, too, heard the siren. Joseph Jager, an Anne Arundel County police officer, drove his patrol car to the north parking lot, stopped, and got out. Jager was one of the original "paid chauffeurs" at the Brooklyn Fire Station and no stranger to fire. He had seen the flames from the rear of the building as he was cruising along Belle Grove Road.[14]

People who had been injured and burned were wandering about the parking lot. Not wasting a second of precious time, Jager picked up his two-way radio and requested his dispatch center in the town of Ferndale, just northwest of Glen Burnie, to send every available ambulance and police officer to the scene.[15]

Back inside the large crowd, described by many as a "tide of humanity," forced its way toward the main entrance to the facility. Many were thinking: "Since this doorway was the way in it must be the quickest way out." Some tried to retrieve their coats from the cloakroom adjacent to the exit. As a result, people started stacking up at the door, creating a huge bottleneck that slowed the evacuation.[16]

As choking smoke engulfed the inside of the hall, and hot flames rolled overhead, people pushed and shoved their way to the exits more forcefully. Overturned tables and chairs and broken glass were everywhere, causing a great many injuries and obstructing attempts to get out quickly. A few men stood on tables and tried to calm the crowd, but it was of little use.[17]

Suddenly, all of the lights in the hall went out. The panic increased enormously as hundreds now tried to fight their way to the exits. Anyone pushed to the floor was trampled. The *News-Post* reported the next day that survivors were still trembling hours after their escape. One described the scene as "the most terrible thing imaginable." Lawrence O'Brien, the oyster roast's chairman, was stunned. He later said, "Men behaved like beasts. I saw men beating women to get into a door or window. Men and women shrieked, screamed, and cried — I will never forget it."[18]

The largest exit opening, designed to evacuate 250 people per minute, was located between the milk bar and the huge hall. In order to keep non-paying customers from coming into the event, the door had been locked on this evening.[19] The door had no panic hardware, no metal bar that when depressed pops and releases the locking bolt.

Thomas Hare of Brooklyn and Clarence Libno, an off-duty Baltimore County police sergeant, somehow broke open the doors, thereby saving hundreds of lives. People stampeded out of this opening, rushing through and over the counters of the milk bar and finally out the milk bar door and windows.[20]

Those still inside took matters into their own hands. The cloakroom was soon overrun, and people tried to climb through its windows. Many broke out glass panes with their fists, severely cutting their hands in the process. The crowd broke down Roy Helms's office door and swarmed in, seeking escape through the office windows. Some found a doorway leading from the office to the milk bar and got out that way.[21]

The hall's windows were very difficult to climb through. Framed in metal, they were five feet off the floor and had a large sash near the middle that opened outward.[22] Desperate parents tossed their children through these openings.

Nine-year-old Monette Obzut was thrown out a window by her mother as flames swept the ceiling overhead. Suffering from shock, Monette rode to South Baltimore General Hospital in a private car driven by Mary Brandt and later joined up with her mother who was being treated for burns. Jack Daughtery pushed his wife Ester safely out a door and later escaped through a window. Unfortunately he would never see his wife alive again.[23]

Someone unlocked the exit door to the cocktail lounge, permitting many to get out through there. Others got out through the kitchen, the north, south, and west exit doors, and the large opened overhead door on the east wall.[24]

Frank Kvech III and his small party saw at least four women trapped in the fenced-in area behind the kitchen. The roof over the kitchen was blazing, and the women were close to being badly burned. Heavy fire was also coming from a vent in the exterior wall above the east wall overhead door.[25] Aided by others, Frank reached over the six-foot-high fence gate and helped the women escape by grabbing each under the arms and one by one pulling them over the top of the locked gate.

While young Frank aided the women on the east side of the hall, his father was performing extraordinary deeds in the smoke on the opposite side of the building, at a second overhead door on the west wall of the hall. The weight of people pushing up against it bent the door outward, which

Men Acted 'Like Beasts,' Fire Survivor Declares

hampered its operation.[26] To make matters worse, the door was still locked, forcing many people to try to get out by crawling through windows on the west wall. Somehow, Frank Kvech Jr. fought his way to the overhead door, found the latching mechanism, and released it. He opened the large door despite its distortion, allowing many more to escape the inferno.[27]

Not far from where Frank Kvech was fighting the bent overhead door on the west side was a very frightened Lou Sokolis. About fifteen feet away from the door that led through the cocktail lounge, and with flames above her, she kicked off her high heeled shoes to move faster and started to fight her way to the opening. One of the men who had knocked her down moments before was hurling his body against the crowd to get out the door. Lou grabbed on to him and the two of them entered into a violent dance. Bouncing back and forth and holding on to each other, they eventually made their way through the crowd and outside. One of the three men who had almost killed her moments before had inadvertently saved her life.

Obeying their first instincts, fear-stricken patrons fought, pushed, and shoved their way to fresh air and refuge from the flames, but once outside, some tried to reenter, thereby obstructing the masses trying to get out and causing additional confusion and panic. Professor John L. Bryan, head of the Fire Protection Curriculum at the University of Maryland at the time, studied the Arundel Park panic behavior. He attributes the reentry to people looking for or wanting to assist friends and family. His study also reveals that in the early stages of the fire, when those who realized that there was a problem went back to alert their friends, they were laughed at. Many believed that the fire was isolated and not life threatening. Dr. Bryan also surmised that the large amount of alcohol consumed throughout the afternoon undoubtedly affected judgment and perception of the impending situation.[28]

As Frank Kvech III and his group were rescuing the women from the

The east side of Arundel Park, not far from where Frank Kvech III rescued four women trapped behind the kitchen fence. (Patrick Prendergast.)

fenced-in area by the kitchen, he saw his father's green 1954 Chevrolet parked near the kitchen wall. Firefighters arrived and said the car would have to be moved. The heat had already blistered the paint and broken the front door window on the passenger side. It was at that moment that Frank realized his father might still be in the building.

Frank quickly sized up the situation and considered going back in and looking for his father. He peered into the large opening of the overhead door but saw no one. The interior lights were out and the smoke pouring through the opening was as black as coal. He was walking toward the door when his father came around the corner of the building. They greeted one another with profound relief, and Frank's dad jumped in the now scorched Chevrolet and drove it to a safer spot out of the way.[29]

Another person who safely made her way out was Stella Kozlowski of Baltimore. But, for some reason known only to her, Stella re-entered the hall.[30]

One lucky survivor was Veronica Sparrow. "I could feel the flames on the back of my neck," she would recall later. "I kept saying to myself, this is it, this is it. All I could think about was a friend of mine who was there with four small children. Then, finally, I got pulled out of a door." Thirty-year-old Conrad Griffin, a lathe operator, said, "my wife and I were able to escape through one of the smaller doors since they couldn't open the larger [overhead] door."[31]

Al Barthelme, the former coach of Baltimore's professional basketball team, the Bullets, was inside the building when the flames broke loose. He said, "the scene at one window was a real panic. With everybody trying to get out of one window, it was pretty brutal." Barthelme added, "Some were pulled back by others as they started through, some were even throwing out of windows friends they didn't think could make it any other way."[32]

A Brooklyn Park barber, August Marcellino, severely slashed his wrists breaking window glass in his attempt to escape. Thirty-three-year-old Kathryn Gilligan, who lived in Green Haven, along with Marcellino's wife were among at least a dozen people Marcellino was credited with saving. He stood on top of a bar near one of the windows to calm everyone within earshot, broke the window with his fist, and forced people through. Marcellino himself, "almost suffocating from the choking smoke," climbed out the window and collapsed in the slush-covered parking lot.[33]

Twenty-seven-year-old Lettie Andrews of Severna Park said, "I owe my life to two men who bodily threw me out of a window." Like Lou Sokolis and so many other women, Andrews was knocked to the floor and trampled by the mob. "Every time I tried to get up to the window," she said, "the panicking crowd would knock me down." Exhausted, Andrews lay on the floor screaming and crying until discovered and rescued by two men.[34]

Leo Rust of Brooklyn had seen many fires over the years throughout the numerous Fairfield oil refineries near his work, but none like this. "The fire spread like someone poured gasoline all over the place — worse than any refinery fire I have experienced. The smoke was so thick you couldn't see over twenty feet. I fell at the door and people trampled on me trying to get out." Fortunately before he fell, Rust was able to get his wife and two daughters to safety. Many said they heard an explosion as a blast of flame swept through the hall.[35]

One of the worst moments of the tragedy involved Anne Arundel County Commissioner John M. Everd. When he saw the fire race across the hall's ceiling, Everd escaped by jumping through a window on the west side of the structure.[36] As Frank Kvech Jr. was struggling to open the large overhead door inside, Everd assisted from the outside. After the flood of bodies rushed through, he shouted to anyone who might have been trapped in the smoke to come in the direction of his voice. Approximately ten people heard his call and escaped thanks to his efforts.

Everd stayed in the doorway until the flames singed his hair. As he started to walk away from the structure, he glanced up to the window through which he had escaped moments earlier and saw the face of a women inside who had managed to raise herself up to the sill. It appeared that she would jump through, but, Everd said, "she lost her grip on the hot metal window sash . . . and fell back into the flames."[37]

7

Black Snow and Crimson Skies

Half a mile to the east, at the Brooklyn Park Fire Station, it seemed to eighteen-year-old Harry Zlotowski like the start of another quiet Sunday evening. Harry had just completed Les Helfrich's practical session of the training course and was helping Les clean up after the class. A number of volunteers were on hand.[1]

The call from Arundel Park came in at 5:08 P.M. According to Volunteer Lieutenant Charles Doegen, who would later become Brooklyn's fire chief, the party calling said "we have a small fire down here at Arundel Park. Will you send us one fire truck?" Doegen wrote down the information. Another member switched on the county fire radio system and dispatched the address and situation to the surrounding fire companies. A building fire, regardless of what the person on the phone requested, required a standard response of four companies.[2]

Eddie Utz started up the US open-cab pumper, turned on the red flashing lights, and drove out the station door with Lieutenant Doegen riding in the right front officer's seat. Harry Zlotowski, Ron Hasse, and Jim File were hanging onto the back step. They headed for Belle Grove Road, while pumper trucks from the Linthicum, Ferndale, and Glen Burnie fire companies also responded.[3]

When Brooklyn's pumper truck turned onto 5th Avenue from Ritchie

Brooklyn's #1 pumper, the "US," pictured here in Baltimore in the early Fifties at the "I am an American Day Parade," was the first engine to arrive at the Arundel Park fire. (Photograph by Fred Wilson. Courtesy of Gary Utz.)

Highway and approached the crest of the 5th Avenue hill, the crew spotted a large column of black smoke. As the engine descended the hill to Belle Grove Road, Joe and Peg Ross of 5th Avenue were among the many in Brooklyn Park who heard the sirens, went outside, and saw the billowing column of smoke. "On that day we never saw or heard so many fire engines and ambulances in our lives," the Rosses said later.[4] Nothing could have prepared the firefighters for what they were about to confront.

The Brooklyn pumper truck made its way south past 6th Avenue and started down the hill toward Arundel Park. Utz maneuvered along Belle Grove Road, now backed up with carloads of people, later estimated to have numbered in the thousands, who were trying to help fight, or simply watch, the fire. Lieutenant Doegen could see flames coming from the rear of the building.

Before the firefighters could make any attempt to fight the fire they first had to deal with the hundreds of parked vehicles and others trying to drive out of the lot. Making matters worse were the severely injured victims who had managed to get out and were now milling about in shock.[5]

After much maneuvering, Ed Utz was able to position the pumper midway

Brooklyn's #2 pumper, the "Mack," pictured here in Baltimore at the "I am an American Day Parade," was the second engine to arrive at the fire and pumped from the closest fire hydrant, which was approximately three hundred feet south of the building. (Photo by Fred Wilson. Courtesy of Gary Utz.)

Linthicum VFD's Ford pumper, pictured here in 1965, was utilized to draft much needed water from the large pond on the east side of Belle Grove Road. Notice the pump mounted on the front bumper, making the unit ideal for drafting operations. (Tom German.)

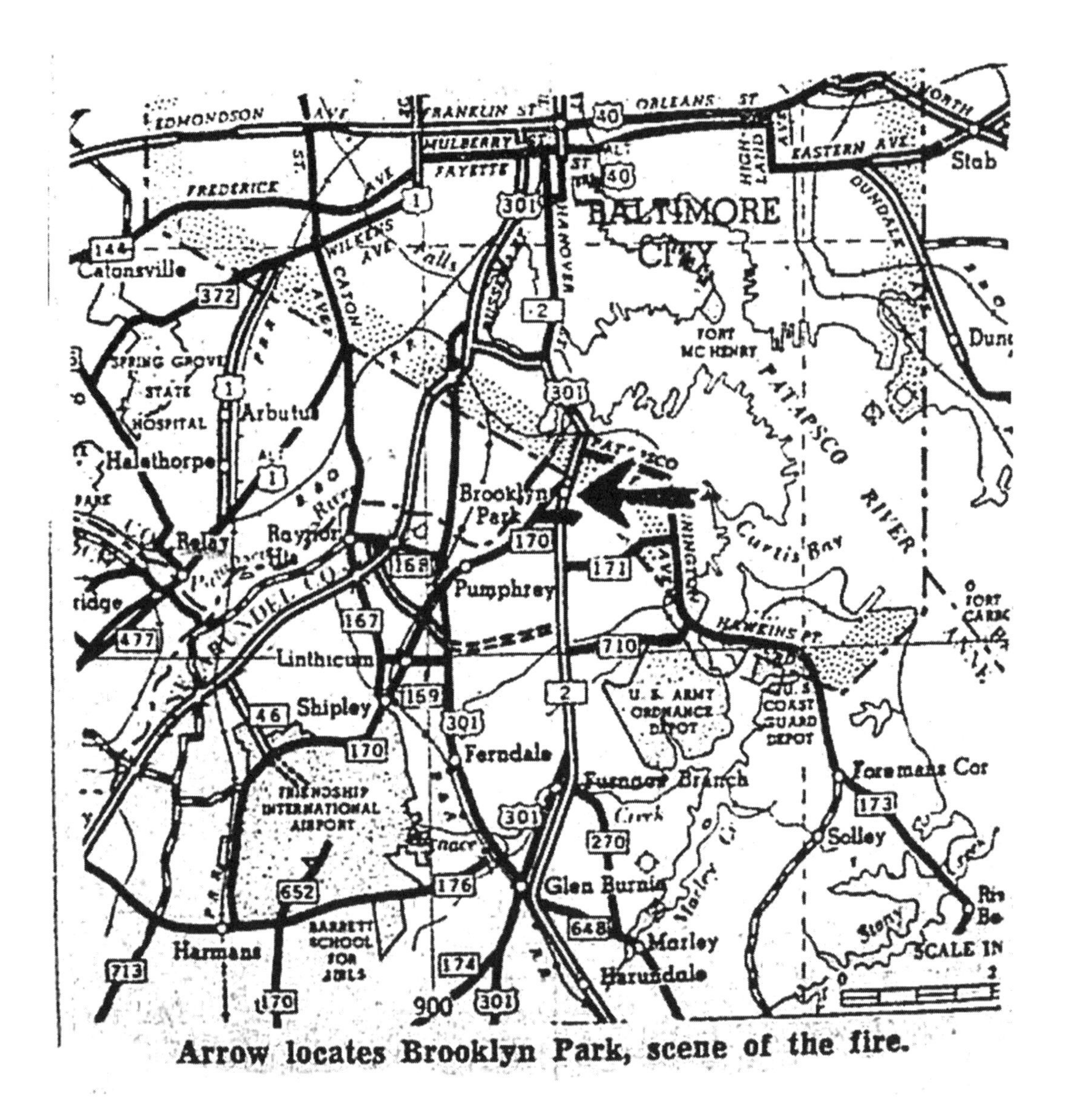

Undated newspaper map.

between the burning structure and the fire hydrant located approximately three hundred feet south of the building. Within minutes of their arrival, the crew had pulled the attack hose lines and advanced them to the fire. These lines were supplied from the pumper's 750-gallon tank. Larger hose lines were dragged back and hooked up to the fire hydrant to augment the water supply.[6]

When Lieutenant Doegen took the initial phone call from Arundel Park

Linthicum VFD's "Little Mack" in front of Linthicum's station on Camp Meade Road with Engineman Tom German in 1965. During the fire the "Little Mack" was positioned on the west side of the building and operated very close to the large overhead door on the Belle Grove Road side of the building. (Tom German.)

at the fire station, Brooklyn's second engine, the newer 1947 open-cab Mack pumper, was backed up to the small metal storage building in the rear. Les Helfrich and others were putting dry hose in the hose bed to replace wet and dirty hose used earlier during the firemen's training class.[7]

Helfrich, who many years later would retire as an assistant chief with the Baltimore City Fire Department, was overseeing the hose replacement. As Utz went out the door with the US pumper, someone ran back to the metal building and shouted, "Lets go, there's a fire at Arundel Park!" Les Helfrich, Captain John Anderson, Norman Ray, and the rest of the crew sped off for Belle Grove Road in the Mack pumper.[8]

By the time Les turned the big Mack pumper onto Belle Grove Road, he was not far from Brooklyn Park's first engine. He had no trouble maneuvering his engine through the parking lot, but when he approached the fire hydrant on the east side of the building he found a car parked in front of it. Seeing the flames roll up the back of the main hall's large Quonset roof and recognizing the danger of the situation, Les eased the engine's big front bumper into the car and pushed it away from the hydrant.[9] The maneuver worked, allowing Les to connect the large 4.5-inch, soft-sleeve, reinforced cotton hose from the engine's pump to the hydrant. Unfortunately for the owner of the car, Les had pushed it close to an embankment, and it slid over the side into a small ditch. Far more importantly, the supply lines for the first engine could now be charged with much needed water and pressure.[10]

To the south, Engineman Donald Amrhein, driving Linthicum's 1950 Ford pumper truck and crew, with red and white lights flashing and the siren wailing, was speeding north on Camp Meade Road and nearing the intersection of Belle Grove Road and Baltimore and Annapolis (B&A) Boulevard. Traditionally, Linthicum, the closest fire station to the Belle Grove Road corridor after Brooklyn, could always be counted upon to be the second to arrive, but not on this day.[11] On reaching the intersection, the Ford pumper, outfitted with a new experimental overhead V-8 gasoline engine, backfired loudly as Amrhein downshifted and pumped the brakes. Ferndale's Engineman Willie Hubers had radioed ahead. They were just about at the intersection, and the Linthicum unit was required to grant right of way.

As Amrhein brought the Linthicum engine almost to a stop, Ferndale's new Ward La France open-cab white and red pumper truck rolled through the intersection from B&A Boulevard and turned north onto Belle Grove Road. Jager's radio report to the Ferndale Police Station, which simultaneously notified the fire station across the street, had given the Ferndale volunteers a big jump on the call.[12]

The early police contact and the ability to see the black column of smoke from the top of the B&A Boulevard hill meant there was no stopping the Ferndale engine and crew. By the time Donald Amrhein could shift through the Linthicum pumper's gears and regain his speed, the Ferndale engine was negotiating the sharp curve on Belle Grove Road and was soon out of sight.[13]

At the fire ground, firefighters were doing everything in their power to get water to the fire. Their first job was to move the many cars still parked near the main hall. In order to release the parking brakes, the men had to smash car windows. Gary Utz, currently with the Anne Arundel County Fire Department, remembers his dad, Ed, recounting how they broke the windows on vehicles that could not be moved and ran hose lines right through the interiors."[14]

At 5:16 P.M., five minutes after Brooklyn's pumper trucks had arrived, Lieutenant Doegen could see that the building's interior was completely engulfed and that fire was breaking through the huge Quonset-style roof. Doegen radioed back to the station and requested the second and third alarms, to bring additional equipment and manpower.[15]

Engines already at the scene were positioned around the burning structure to provide the best points for applying hose streams on the fire. It soon became evident that the water from Arundel Park's lone hydrant would not be enough.

After following the Ferndale pumper to the front of the building near the main entrance, the Linthicum pumper was ordered by one of Brooklyn's officers to lay a water supply hose line from the west end of the building to a pond along a dirt road west of Belle Grove Road. At the pond, the Linthicum engine would set up a suction-draft.[16]

With injured people milling all around it, Amrhein put the engine in reverse and backed through a very narrow corridor between parked vehicles and arriving police cars to an area near the west end of the building. As the unit was backing, Will Morrison, an eighteen-year-old volunteer with the Linthicum organization, could see people still climbing out the windows of the blazing and smoke-filled structure. Through those windows he could also see large pieces of burning fiberboard ceiling falling to the floor.

Will then saw an off-duty Baltimore City firefighter put a coat over his head and run back into the inferno in hopes of finding those who were still trapped. He disappeared into the flames and smoke. About thirty seconds later he reappeared, alone. Will described the scene as mass confusion.[17]

Having turned his engine around, Amrhein drove the Ford pumper across Belle Grove Road to lay the hose supply line to the pond. Simultaneously, Linthicum's second engine, a 1948 opened-cab Mack pumper truck pulled up from Belle Grove Road. The Mack's volunteer engineman, Edgar Ford, who would become Linthicum's fire chief in the mid-1960s and later enjoy a successful career with the Anne Arundel County Police Department, connected the end of Amrhein's supply line to his pump. Linthicum's

Overleaf: Arundel Park at the height of the blaze. Fire fighting crews apply hose streams through the window of the cloak room in the front of the building. (Courtesy of the Hearst Corporation.)

crew immediately directed hose streams at the fire at the west end of the building.[18]

Linthicum's Ford pumper had a unique feature. Unlike Brooklyn's engine, the one Frank Homberg used to draft from a nearby pond the previous summer, the Ford's pump was mounted not in the middle of the vehicle but on its front bumper in front of the engine. Its ability to drive right up to the edge of the pond made it the ideal unit to draft water. While hooking up the hose tubes of hard rubber reinforced with wire that are necessary to draft water from a pond or other body of standing water, Donald Amrhein looked out toward the pond and could not believe his eyes.

A young volunteer who had accompanied him to the draft site along the dirt road had carelessly walked out onto the ice-covered pond in all the excitement and was busy chopping through the ice with a pick-end axe. Amrhein ordered him to stop at once and make a hole closer to shore—thereby probably averting another casualty of the fire. The hard tube with a metal strainer attached was dropped in, and moments later critically needed water was on its way to the fire.

As other county fire units arrived, their drivers positioned them around the building. A set of double hose supply lines was laid in the street, and engines pumped water from the hydrant on the corner of 6th Avenue and Belle Grove Road. Eventually a general alarm was requested. Ambulances, fire apparatus, and equipment came from Pikesville, Baltimore City, and as far away as Deale in southern Anne Arundel County.[19]

Back at the fire, an off-duty police officer was pulling a smoking Andrew Brady out from a small opening, only about a foot high, between the floor and the lower edge of the west side overhead door, which had become stuck. Brady's hands, buttocks, and head were severely burned. The leather headband from his incinerated uniform cap was still affixed to his head. Brady had reentered the building at least nine times, making rescues and helping people to safety outside, but his last mission had overwhelmed him. The inside of the hall was filled with deadly flames and dark, acrid smoke.

The policeman dragged Brady to his personal car. Moments later he was racing to South Baltimore General Hospital with Special Police Officer Brady in severe pain lying across the back seat. Brady would be the first casualty to arrive.[20]

As Brady was being sped to the hospital, the only thing firefighters

In this grainy, unidentified newspaper photograph, firefighters direct hoses through one of the overhead doors into the building.

could do was train their hose lines on the windows and doorways to protect anyone who had somehow made it that far. But it soon became horribly clear that all who were going to get out were now outside, and that anyone left inside could not survive the smoke and superheated temperatures as the fire raced on to consume the entire structure.[21]

According to Captain John Anderson, riding on the second Brooklyn engine, "There was so much confusion at one point, we thought we had over a hundred people trapped inside."[22] Three brave Brooklyn firefighters tied to ropes crawled into the back of the building to search the bathrooms after hearing reports that some people were trapped there. They could find no one.[23] Other arriving firefighters, together with numerous county and state police officers, provided first aid to the hundreds of victims who were suffering from severe cuts, burns, and shock.[24]

Long-time Brooklyn Park resident Norman Ray, a volunteer with the Brooklyn Fire Company, was home on weekend leave from the Navy the night of the fire. Arriving on the second engine with Helfrich and Anderson, Ray remembers breaking out car windows and windshields in order to move cars and advance the supply hose to the fire. Once the supply hose was stretched to Brooklyn's Engine No. 1 (the US), Ray hurried back to the engine at the fire hydrant to assist Helfrich in hooking up the hose lines. Eventually he joined the crews directing water on the fire with the hand-held hose lines.

Responding to and fighting the massive fire was just one of a number of challenges for Norman Ray on this cold Sunday evening. He soon realized that he had to report back to his naval duty post. Rushing back to the Brooklyn Park Fire Station, he just managed to catch the last bus on Ritchie Highway going south to Norfolk. It would be many hours later, at the Norfolk Naval Shipyard, before Ray could clean up from the fire.[25]

On 6th Avenue, about a quarter of a mile north of the fire, five-year-old Michael Ripnick, his little brother Richard, and their parents Mary and Gordon, were enjoying a typical Sunday afternoon watching the nine-inch Admiral console television set and reading the papers. On hearing the sirens, Michael got up and looked out his front window. He remembers seeing flakes of "black snow" falling on 6th Avenue and throughout the neighborhood.[26]

The black snow was created when Arundel Park's tar-coated roof, more than fourteen thousand square feet of it, disintegrated in the flames. Winds created by the hot and fast-moving fire sent pieces of tar-coated felt high into the evening sky. Deputy Chief Frank Homberg would later state in an interview that embers from the fire landed more than a mile and a half away.[27] After joining Michael at the window and seeing for himself the smoke, flames, and black snow, Mike's father Gordon, the Marine veteran, put on his coat and headed out the door to see if he could help.[28]

Shortly after 5 P.M., Wally Sokolis, Louise's older brother, was sitting down to dinner with his parents, Joe and Lorraine, in their 4th Street home just about a mile and a half east of Arundel Park. From the kitchen they could hear the Brooklyn Park fire house siren in the distance.

Wally and his parents had heard the siren many times over the years at their Arundel Village row home, but on this night the siren wailed continuously. Never before had they heard it go through so many cycles. Wally got up and looked out his front door. As he gazed over the roofs of the neatly aligned red brick rowhouses across his street, he couldn't believe his eyes.

Lt. Charlie Doegen and another fire fighter pull down smoldering ceiling with a pike pole. Notice the height of the window sills from the floor, making it extremely difficult for escape. (Lorretta Kane Dove.)

A darkening winter sky over the southwest was now filled with brilliant shades of red, like a gorgeous sunset on a warm summer night. Wally had never seen a winter sky like it before. He too put on a coat, ran out of the house, jumped into his 1939 Nash, and drove up to Church Street. He followed Church Street since it seemed to lead straight toward that bright red glow.

When he reached Ritchie Highway, the police had closed the intersection. A parade of fire engines, ambulances, police cars, and rescue trucks from communities around the county were racing north on Ritchie Highway en route to the fire. Somehow, Wally was able to get behind one of the engines and followed it all the way to the vicinity of 5th Avenue and Belle Grove Road, where he competed with many others trying to find a parking spot. He then ran the remaining half-mile down to the fire.

Frederick Evans, one of the Brooklyn Volunteer Fire Company's ambulance drivers, said the sky looked like it had been "dyed crimson." People throughout Brooklyn claim the sky was "lit up" that night. Those who saw it would never forget it.[29]

At the Brooklyn Fire Station on 5th Street and Pontiac Avenue in the city, the firefighters heard banging on the station's front doors. A small group of frantic people outside told them of a massive fire in Anne Arundel County just across the city line. The firefighters could only tell them to go back and pull the alarm on the fire alarm street box at Jeffery Street between Hanover and 2nd Streets, the nearest one to the Baltimore City–Anne Arundel County line.

About 5:00 p.m., Baltimore City's fire alarm office was swamped with telephone calls reporting a raging fire at Arundel Park near the city line. Although an official request from the county had not been received, the Baltimore City Fire Alarm Office decided to send Engine 10 (Fairfield), Engine 26 (West Street), Truck 21 (Brooklyn), Ambulance 9, and the Acting 6th Battalion Chief (Captain John McKinley, Engine 12) to the scene.[30]

One of the alarm calls was received at 5:20 p.m. The caller was former State Delegate August C. Myers. Gasping and coughing, Myers was inside Arundel Park's cocktail lounge. He said, "People are hysterical. They're piling up at the doors. Hundreds are trapped — God it's awful. I've got to get out of here, the smoke is killing me — I can't talk."[31]

The "old fire horse," Frank Homberg, the other career pump operator assigned to the Brooklyn Park Station, was also at the time the Volunteer Deputy Chief. His son, Frank Homberg Jr., a retired division chief with the Anne Arundel County Fire Department, remembers that on that evening his father was sick in bed with the flu. But when he heard about the fire and the massive traffic jam around the burning assembly hall, the elder man got out of bed, dressed, and the two of them walked across 11th Avenue from their house to the fire station to retrieve Frank Sr.'s protective gear.

Father and son then walked a quarter of a mile through their Brooklyn Park neighborhood and then through the snow-covered woods to the fire, where they worked into the small hours of the morning. Although Frank Jr. was not yet a member of the department, he helped his father by running messages between the chiefs and their crews working the hose lines and searching for victims.[32]

As additional engines arrived, hose lines were stretched for both water supply and fire attack. Other engines shuttled water from hydrants located blocks away back down to the fire scene. Altogether Baltimore City, Anne Arundel, Baltimore, Howard, and Prince George's Counties, along with the Friendship Airport Fire Department, sent a total of thirty-four fire engines, two ladder trucks, seven rescue trucks, and fifteen ambulances.[33]

It was later estimated that five thousand spectators also arrived at the scene, many with their vehicles, all of which hampered the responding emergency equipment.[34] It was a major challenge for police to keep a traffic lane open so that ambulances could move in and out.

Newspapers quoted Chief Fire Marshal Harry Klasmeier as saying "The citizens mobilized quicker than the fire departments did!"[35] It was later determined that a major reason for the community's response was a series of news flashes that appeared on local television channels and radio stations throughout the evening.[36] One can also safely assume that because of the number of oyster roasts being held throughout the Baltimore area on that Sunday, and the fact that some families were not really certain which one their friends or relatives were attending, many of those who descended upon Brooklyn's Arundel Park feared for their loved ones.

Based on the Arundel Park building's dimensions, combustible construction, and fire involvement, over four thousand gallons of water per minute would have been required to extinguish the fire quickly.[37] That in turn would have required more than fifty firefighters and seventeen large hose lines over and above what the Brooklyn fire station crew could provide. Yet even had those resources been available, there is no guarantee that any lives would have been saved. The ability to acquire that much water and to apply it to the fire in time would be impossible even with today's technology, standards, and capabilities.

Overleaf: Arundel Park after the fire. (Courtesy of Gary Utz.)

Inset: The closest fire hydrant, three hundred feet south of the building, the day after the fire. (Charlie Doegen and Les Helfrich.)

8

Survivors and Victims

What had been panic and pandemonium inside was now mass confusion outside. Many of the injured had collapsed or fainted in the parking lot and along Belle Grove Road. Some wandered around in a daze. The temperature was only thirty-eight degrees that evening, and most of those who had been inside the hall were without coats and hats. Some had even lost their shoes. One woman said her shoes had been burned off her feet.[1]

It soon became apparent that not everyone had made it out. As some of the survivors realized their spouses and loved ones were not outside the building, they frantically began searching for them. Survivors agonized as they watched the last few people bail out of the broken windows and roll out the exit doors that were now filled with billowing brown-black smoke interlaced with orange flames. They prayed to see the familiar faces they had so convivially accompanied into the building only a few hours earlier.

The one person who was in the best position to describe the scene was *Maryland Gazette* newspaper reporter Harry Smith. As he saw the first engines responding to the fire along Ritchie Highway, he decided to follow them as he had so many times in the past. On most of his fire response adventures, he would arrive at the scene shortly after the fire apparatus only to find a smoldering mattress, a pot of burned food, or an apologetic housewife explaining that the flames she thought she had seen across the street in the window of a brick row house were just the glare from the sun.[2]

But not today. Today, as he drove down the Belle Grove Road hill near 6th Avenue and rounded the curve heading south, he could not believe his eyes. The flames driving upward from the back of Arundel Park's roof presented a spectacular sight. Still, bad as it looked, he thought it was just a big structure fire.

Smith parked his car along Belle Grove Road so as not to be pinned in by the arriving fire engines and hurried over to the west side of the building nearest the two-lane highway, now packed with cars and pickup trucks that had brought the curious, thrill-seekers, shocked family members, and those who had genuinely good intentions of helping out in any way they could.

Smith peered into the smoke-filled exit door on the west side. Later he described it as "an entrance to a dark, fearsome cave."[3] He was told the place was clear, but that idea vanished when he saw the faces of the survivors. Men embraced screaming women. Some men cried, and all stared in horror at the burning building. Many sobbed or called out for missing relatives. Many would go on looking in vain. Some could only stare, dazedly repeating a name as they lived private nightmares. Shivering women stood there shoeless with only nylon stockings between their feet and the cold, slushy mud.

The heat was intense. Smith noticed that county police officer Robert W. Griffith had parked his black and white patrol car about fifteen feet from the front of the building. As the flames belched forth, Griffith, who would retire as a division chief of fire investigation with the Anne Arundel County Fire Department in the late 1970s, hurried back to move his cruiser to a safer spot.[4]

An off-duty Baltimore County police officer approached Smith and told him, "As far as I know, there's nobody in there. Pray they're all out. Pray!" One man told Smith he had tried to pull a woman out a window by her arm and her flesh had come off. The man told the three other women with her to abandon her and jump out the window. They didn't.[5]

It was at this point that the desperate realized the nightmare was far from over and that it might never end. The unthinkable and the unimaginable

Overleaf: Firefighters and ambulance attendants in front of Arundel Park look on as crews struggle to obtain additional water while fire consumes the building. (Courtesy of the Hearst Corporation.)

Catonsville
V.F.D

MILK

Officials and worried relatives congregate outside the milk bar after the fire had been suppressed. (Courtesy of Patrick Prendergast.)

had been thrust upon them. They spoke in trembling voices, their only hope now resting in the possibility their relatives, friends, and spouses had been taken to the hospital.

To this day, survivors cannot forget the mixture of helplessness and desperation in the faces of those who could not find their loved ones. The twisted mix of horror, hysteria, and agony has haunted many of the more fortunate ever since. Lou Sokolis knew many of these people from the neighborhood and from other church and social events. Their despair is etched forever in her mind, and today it bothers her more than the inferno that almost took her young life.

As the evening dusk turned to night, ambulance after ambulance crossed the Patapsco River on the Hanover Street Bridge about three miles to the north, carrying the burned, shocked, and lacerated to Baltimore's hospitals. Patients were dropped off and quickly ushered into crowded emergency rooms. Exhausted crews switched the flashing lights on top of their mud-spattered vehicles back on and once more headed south across the bridge and back down Belle Grove Road to the scene of the disaster, where others lay in automobiles or on the muddy ground awaiting transport. Many of the responding units passed one another going in opposite directions. Fortunately on this night, unlike in the past, there would be no drawbridge openings, and no freight train blocked road crossings to impede the emergency responders.

Frederick Evans, one of the ambulance drivers, said that many of the injured were taken to the hospital in private cars. He remembers rendering first aid and transporting five patients on his first trip to South Baltimore General. He made seven trips in all, with a total of thirty-five patients.[6]

Two critically important emergency care providers that evening were Dr. Leonard Flax and Mrs. Julia Bowen, both of Brooklyn Park. Julia Bowen, a nurse who was visiting the event to collect money for the "March of Dimes," assisted Doctor Flax in triage and in administering morphine to the severely burned. According to a Civil Defense report a few months later, Doctor Flax, who lived in the 100 block of 7th Avenue about three blocks from the fire, heard the sirens and saw people passing his house bleeding and screaming. Neighbors had also phoned to alert him of the tragedy. He grabbed his bag, tossed a stethoscope around his neck for identification, and started walking toward the fire. There are two different accounts of how he arrived at the scene. According to one he walked, and it was more than ten minutes before he arrived. The other has it that he hailed down a county police cruiser.[7]

Whatever the case, when he arrived people were still emerging from the building and going back inside. He began treating the wounded as he met them. With the help of police he established an aid station on the ingress road where it entered the parking lot, a spot the ambulances would pass through. Word of his arrival spread rapidly and reassured the crowd.

Not all were calm. At one point a very excited man picked up the doctor's medical bag and ran off with it, saying his mother was bleeding to death. Police were able to recover the bag and report that the woman was not seriously injured.[8]

Julia Bowen and Doctor Flax aided some seventy-five victims. Because of the severity of some of their burns, the doctor quickly went through two bottles of morphine before he could treat all of the patients. He also administered dolophine, demeral, and seconal. With lipstick or ball-point pen, he marked each patient with the type of medication and the time of administration.[9]

The doctor also directed ambulances and told them to which hospital they should go. He asked at least a hundred people with minor injuries not to go to hospitals but to follow up with family physicians in the morning. That probably kept the limited but tenacious weekend staff working in the emergency room at South Baltimore General from being overwhelmed. When he eventually ran out of supplies, Doctor Flax used the Band-Aids, bandages, sterile dressings, alcohol, iodine, smelling salts, and adhesive tape in kits carried on the fire engines and ambulances.[10]

By this time a light, steady drizzle was falling, and many of the injured had been laid on the wet asphalt or mud of the parking lot and covered with what few coats were available. The crowd was described as still dazed, screaming, crying, and praying. Some of the injured ran off and hid behind trees but were soon retrieved and sent to the hospital. One man was described as so violent police had their hands full getting him into an ambulance.[11]

After Lou Sokolis reached safety outside, she realized that the top of her head had been singed. One of her friends had received a nasty cut on her hand from the broken glass. An acquaintance transported both of them to South Baltimore General.

Police directed ambulances arriving along Belle Grove Road into the parking lot. There they lined up at Doctor Flax's makeshift aid station. As soon as the units could be loaded with the shocked, burned, and injured, they were directed back out.[12]

In Baltimore, on Wall, West, and Light Streets around South Baltimore General Hospital, traffic came to a standstill. The hospital, approximately six miles north of Arundel Park, was the closest medical facility to the disaster. Inside, corridors were packed with the injured and their escorts, all competing for and at times demanding treatment for their burns and cuts. Doctors, nurses, and orderlies scurried through the clean tile-walled hallways and treatment rooms to examine and provide care. Transfusions were performed in the corridors.[13]

The hospital sent out a call for additional staff and doctors. Police cruisers, emergency lights flashing and sirens blaring, brought in doctors and nurses from Sinai Hospital. Staff were called back in from home. Many of the off-duty medical workers saw the televised news bulletins or heard about the fire on the radio and rushed to the hospital without waiting to be notified.[14]

From Red Cross headquarters in Washington, a vehicle carrying a hundred pints of blood and a hundred units of serum albumin used for the treatment of shock rushed to Baltimore escorted by police cruisers. At South Baltimore General, special police officers were brought in to control the multitude that was increasing by the minute. The telephone switchboard was besieged with calls. Vital communications could not get out or get in.

Lou Sokolis and her girlfriend were now inside waiting, with images of the tragedy still fresh in their young minds. People wept or fell to their knees praying for loved ones. When it was time for Lou to see the doctor she fainted from shock and exhaustion and collapsed on the floor. Outside, crowds began to gather on the sidewalks waiting for news about their friends or loved ones.[15]

Red Cross and Civil Defense personnel arrived to assist with first aid, locate relatives, and provide coffee and sandwiches to the injured and the anxious who were waiting for information. Two truckloads of soldiers rolled in from one of the local military bases. They had come to give blood.[16]

Doctors and nurses dressed and bandaged burns to the hands, face, head, shoulders, ears, and neck. They treated lacerations, contusions, abrasions, bruises, and injuries to legs, hands, arms, wrists, and ribs. Other patients were treated for smoke inhalation, back injuries, chest pains, nose burns, and shock.[17] Between 6:00 and 6:30 P.M., with at least sixty patients in South Baltimore General's emergency room, the chief resident arrived and took charge. Fortunately, the hospital administrator, director of nursing, anesthetists, dieticians, and other department heads also came in upon hearing the news broadcasts. These key people soon brought order and organization to the chaos.[18]

The chief resident created nine treatment stations and separated the cut and laceration victims from those with burns. He established a control point in the corridor where all patients were identified. Nurses would now have a list that distinguished patients who had received treatment from those who still needed it. Finally, he summoned police cooperation in separating and restraining anxious relatives from the patients. That did not work. Nurses reported that the only way to calm relatives was to link them with the patients they sought. The patients in turn calmed their relatives and friends.[19]

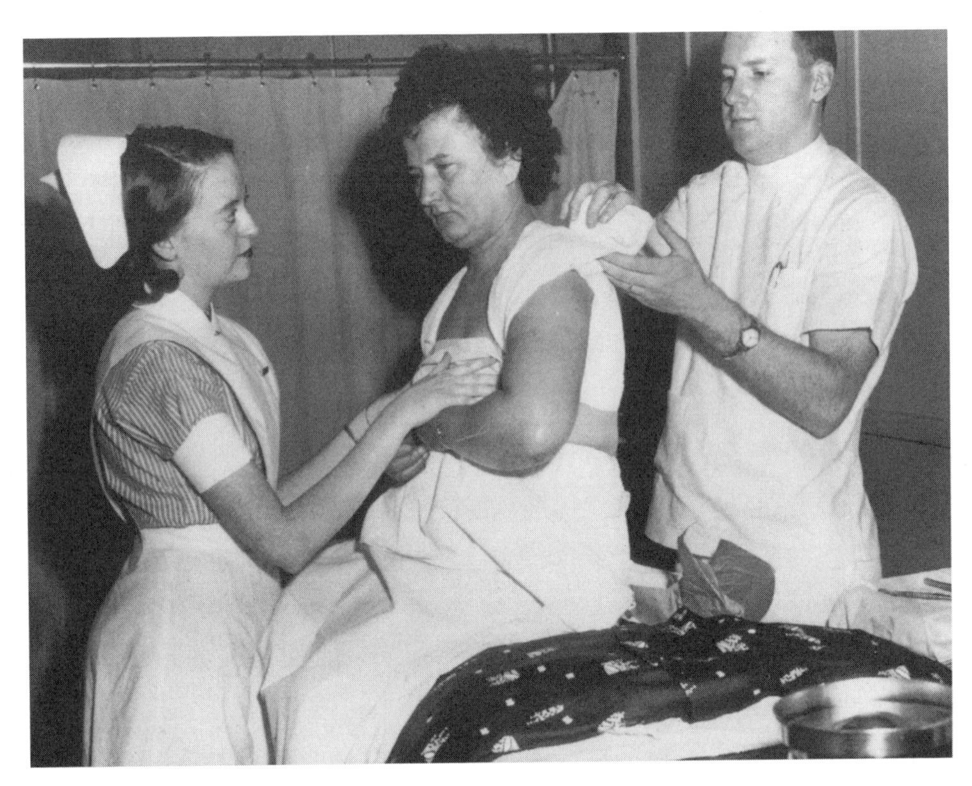

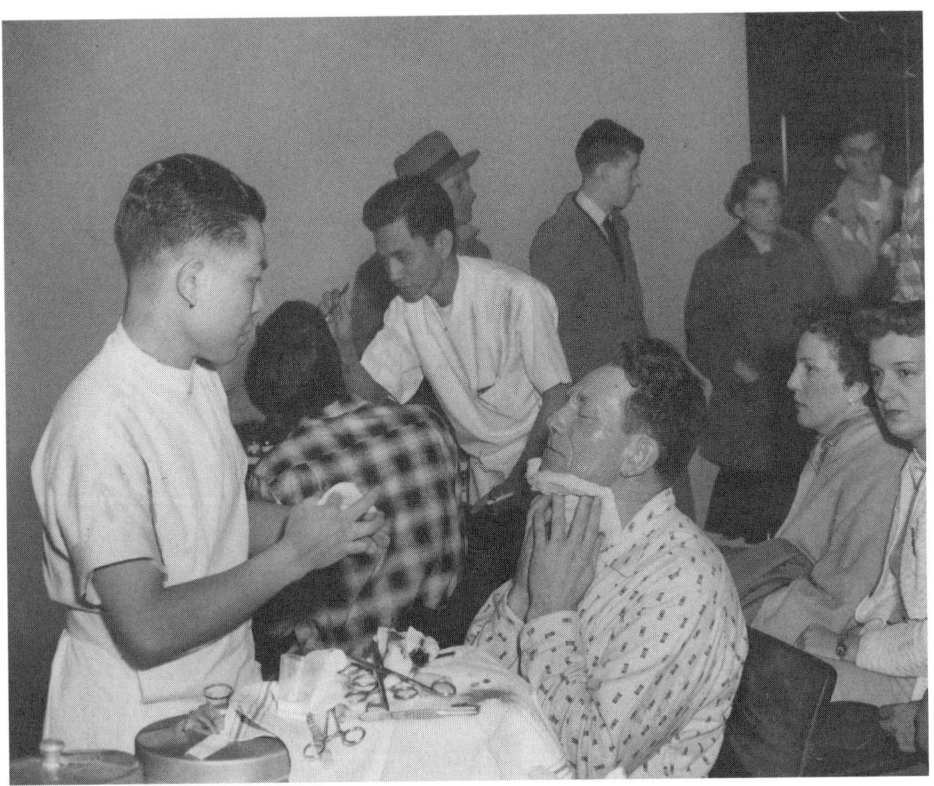

Scenes from area emergency rooms. South Baltimore General Hospital's Dr. Everhard Martin treats M. R. Smith's ear (right). An injured Kathleen Johnson looks on as nurses dress Walter Myer's lacerated hand (below).

Opposite page: Nurse Anne Norton and Dr. Lawrence Pierce of Mercy Hospital treat Veronica Bathon's shoulder burns (top). An orderly at South Baltimore General Hospital treats a victim's burns as other survivors of the fire anxiously await news of loved ones and friends. (All photographs courtesy of the Hearst Corporation.)

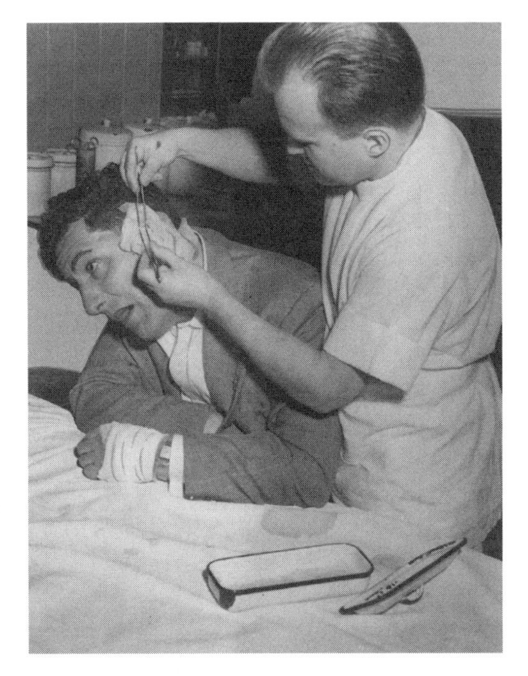

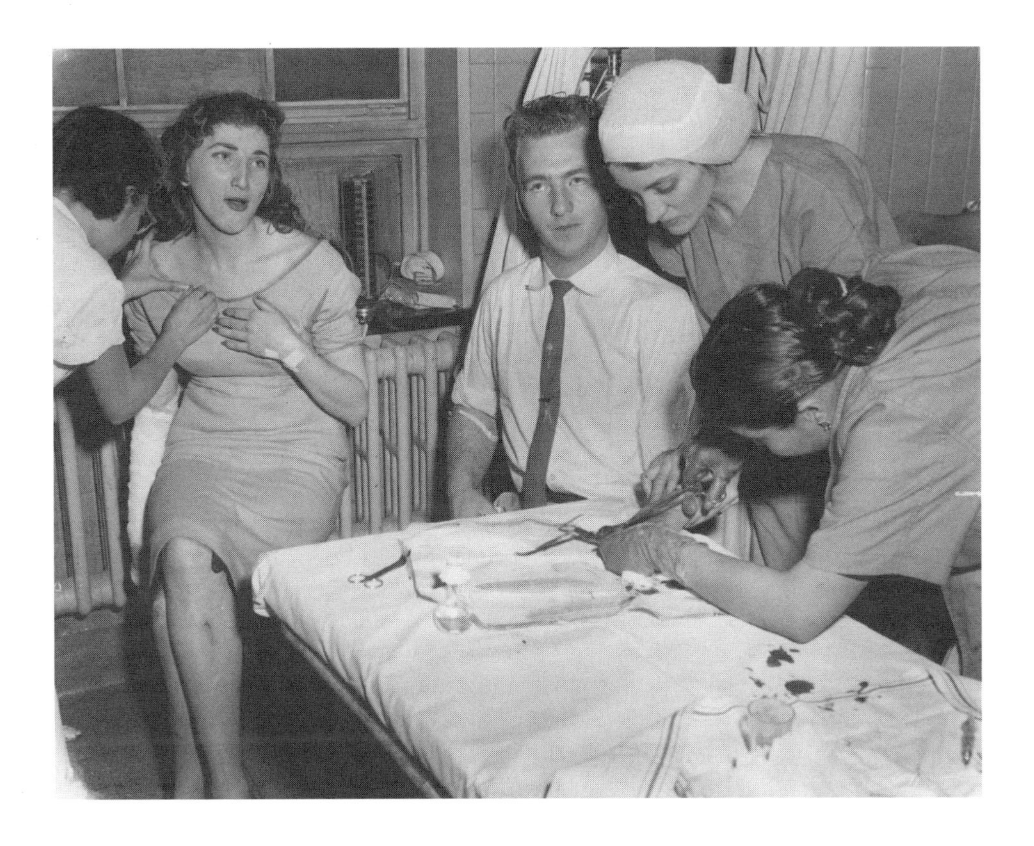

At the Pennington Theater on Pennington Avenue in Curtis Bay, an usher interrupted the movie to announce that there was an emergency phone call for a Mr. Bill Brady. Bill's mother Edith, after hearing the news about her husband, had called to let Bill know that his father had been injured and taken to South Baltimore General. Bill gathered up his family and rushed them home, then headed for the hospital.[20]

Once there, he could scarcely believe the number of people or the degree of confusion in the emergency room. As he moved between people crying, praying, or being cared for by doctors and nurses in the corridor, he passed a man on a stretcher. The man grasped his arm. Bill stopped and stared at the soot-covered victim, whose clothes had been practically burned off his body, trying to figure out why the man wouldn't let go. On looking more closely, he recognized the blue eyes he had looked into only hours before. The man on the stretcher was Andrew Brady Sr.

Ten minutes later, John "Jerry" Thompson had a similar encounter. As Thompson was searching through the emergency room chaos for his wife's father, a voice called out, "Jerry, over here." Having no idea why this dark-skinned man lying on a stretcher was calling his name, he walked over and was shocked to discover it was Andrew Brady Sr., his father-in-law.[21]

Bill asked the doctors why his father was not receiving treatment. They told him privately that his injuries were so severe they could do nothing more for him and were just trying to keep him comfortable.[22]

South Baltimore General received and treated approximately eighty of the injured. Other hospitals in the area were also treating patients. University of Maryland received thirteen, Mercy twelve, Johns Hopkins eleven, Saint Agnes eight, and Lutheran, Church Home, Bon Secours, Sinai, and Franklin Square one each. Saint Joseph received three. Many others were treated at hospitals but left without leaving their names with the staff.[23]

News cameras and reporters added to the chaos inside South Baltimore General. Film was rushed back to the television studios, developed, and aired on special news bulletins that frequently interrupted normal broadcasting during the evening.[24] One bulletin showed Lou Sokolis alive in the hospital corridor waiting for treatment. For her panic-stricken parents at home, glued to the television screen hoping for any information, it was the first news that their daughter had survived. They had not heard from her since she had left the house at noon.

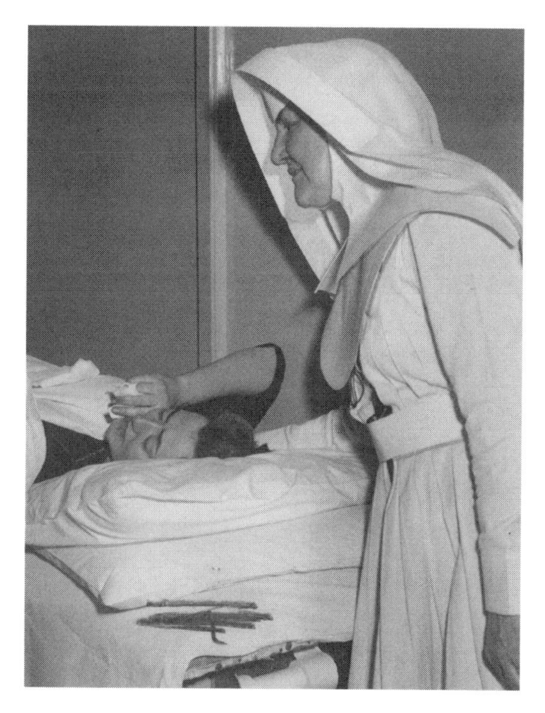

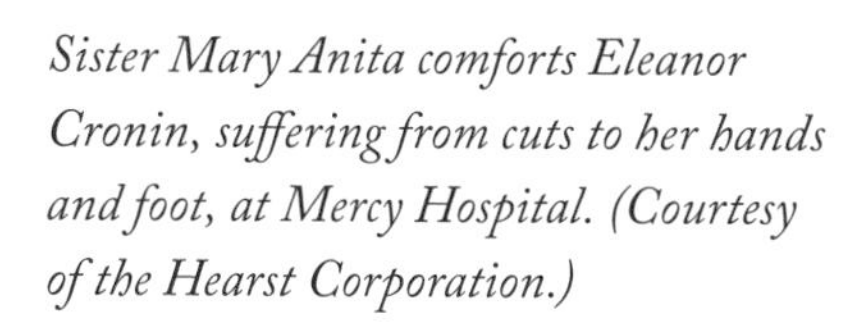

Sister Mary Anita comforts Eleanor Cronin, suffering from cuts to her hands and foot, at Mercy Hospital. (Courtesy of the Hearst Corporation.)

Of the approximately 250 injured, 140 were treated at area hospitals. Fortunately only fourteen had to be admitted. All the others were sent home. The barber, August Marcellino, would undergo a four-hour operation on his wrist and lose the use of one of his hands.[25]

Not long after Joseph Jager of the Anne Arundel County Police Department arrived at Arundel Park, he was backed up by many other county police officers. One, Andrew Brady Jr., pulled up in his patrol car and with Jager and others assisted the firefighters by handling traffic, controlling the crowd, and providing first aid to the injured. Considerable time passed before young Patrolman Brady noticed his father's blue Plymouth abandoned in the parking lot.[26] Not having seen his dad since his arrival, Andrew knew something must have happened to him and asked the help of other officers. They searched the area, questioned survivors, and learned that Andrew Sr. had been transported to South Baltimore General.

Overleaf: At the northeast corner of the building, portable generators supplied electrical power to the many portable utility lights illuminating the fire ground. Black electrical cords lie intertwined with hose lines, as firefighters decide whether it is safe to enter the now roofless structure. (Courtesy of the Hearst Corporation.)

ASFD
E-3

When the fire first broke through the ceiling after his unsuccessful attempt with the fire extinguisher, Andrew Brady Sr., had tried to control the panic. Despite the fierce heat and toxic smoke, Brady had climbed onto a table and tried to calm the crowd by giving directions to the nearest exits. He was the last person to get out of the hall alive, and had left only after doing all he could to be certain that no one alive had been left behind. His courage resulted in third-degree burns on his hands, face, and back.[27]

Others, too, braved the smoke and the flames to assist in the evacuation and aid the victims. Brady's counterpart that evening was August Seifert, a special policeman for the event, volunteer fire fighter, and former chief with the Brooklyn Fire Department. Seifert was also credited with saving many lives.[28] In addition to the special policemen, the priests from Saint Rose of Lima worked diligently to provide first aid to the injured and assist those searching for loved ones.[29]

According to an article that appeared in the University of Maryland's *Fire Service Extension Bulletin* the following May, nineteen off-duty Baltimore City firefighters attended the oyster roast that evening, and when the fire broke out helped wherever they could.[30] Many undertook heroic searches and attempted rescues before and during the arrival of the first fire engines.

Wally Sokolis finally arrived to find firefighting crews well entrenched in battling the fire. He eventually found and joined a team of young volunteers who were having difficulty operating and maneuvering a hose line near the cocktail lounge in the southwest corner of the hall.

For a good number of the younger volunteers, this was their very first fire. Sokolis, remembering his firefighting training from working at the nearby Curtis Bay Coast Guard Yard, helped the younger men pull hose lines and otherwise assisted wherever he could. While doing so he saw a group of people emerge from a wooded area behind the lounge carrying a woman who appeared to be unconscious. This small band of citizen volunteers had turned an old door into a stretcher and were carrying the stricken woman to an available ambulance.[31]

By 7:00 P.M., approximately two hours after the fire had begun, Arundel Park was a smoldering wreck. Groups of firefighters wearing protective equipment and holding numerous hoses, directed streams of water at the fire from pumper trucks all around the structure. Teams advanced hose lines to the windows and doorways in the concrete block walls, which remained intact. A twisted display of metal sashes and louvers warped by the superheated flames still partially obstructed windows whose panes had been smashed out ninety minutes earlier by terrified people fighting one another in their frenzied efforts to escape the flames.[32]

The sound of high-speed gasoline motors drowned out the rumbling V-8 engines on the pumper trucks as portable generators, operating at thousands of revolutions per minute, supplied electrical power to the many portable utility lights illuminating the fire ground. Black electrical cords intertwined with hose lines, hampering firefighters who were contemplating whether it was safe to enter the now roofless structure.

In teams of two or three, firefighters using pike poles (long wooden poles with metal hooks on the end) pushed or pulled down loose concrete blocks near the roof line and what little was left of the thick wooden timbers that once held the massive roof in place. Those hazards had to be addressed before they could make entry.[3]

When the last of the flames had been extinguished, massive clouds of steam and light smoke slowed firefighters as they cautiously entered the ruin and began the grim task of looking for bodies. Hose lines and electric utility lights were now carefully moved into and through the doorway openings.

Smoldering roof timbers, scarred by superheated temperatures and strangulated by bent metal ceiling grid channels and fiberglass insulation, were first drenched with water. Twisted metal from folding tables and chairs made it hazardous to navigate through the smoke and steam. Self-contained breathing apparatus was not yet used in the county fire service, and only a few filter masks were available. The men were accustomed to the acrid smell of burning wood, but that was not all.

As they made the first grim discoveries of the fire's victims, firefighters paused in their work until the more experienced and those in authority could move forward to make a quick examination and note the bodies' locations within the structure. Doctor Flax was summoned and crawled into the smoking ruins with his stethoscope. He pronounced the victims dead at 7:28 P.M.[34]

A priest, John Tribull of Saint Michaels Church in Baltimore, joined Doctor Flax in administering the last rites. Firefighters placed the remains in canvas bags and solemnly carried them to waiting ambulances.[35]

Nine bodies, all women, were found huddled in the northwest quadrant of the building close to the overhead door that Frank Kvech Jr. had managed to force open. One of the bodies was holding a blackened stuffed animal, probably a prize won at one of the money wheels. Another held a tiny toy trumpet in her hand. A tenth body, also a woman, was found on the other side of the building, on the floor between the bandstand and the kitchen.[36]

As the doors were shut in the back of the ambulances, a priest made the sign of the cross and blessed the bodies, which were taken to Singleton's Funeral Home on Crain Highway in Glen Burnie for identification.[37]

While firefighters continued their search for victims and hidden fires throughout the night they were relieved to experience no other major accidents or serious injuries. Firefighter Edward Beck from the Brooklyn Volunteer Fire Station was transported to South Baltimore General with burns on his hands and face.[38] Earlier in the evening, the responding rescue unit from Annapolis City Fire Department had managed to collide with a car on Ritchie Highway at Furnace Branch Road, but damages were relatively minor. The volunteer rescue truck driver was firefighter Nelson Phipps.

Phipps, who was physically huge, was driving the big "Reo" Rescue truck from the "Rescue Hose" Company of Annapolis. After the collision, he actually bent the bumpers of the vehicles, to separate them, with his bare hands. Once the police showed up to make the report, Phipps and crew were back on the truck, painted white with red trim, and on their way to Arundel Park. Nelson Phipps would later enjoy a successful career as a firefighter with Annapolis.[39]

On one of its many return trips from South Baltimore General, the Earliegh Heights ambulance was involved in an accident at West and Charles Streets while transporting a group of blood donors to one of the hospitals. Its front end was badly damaged, and it had to be towed to a garage.[40]

Firefighters and police were not the only organizations assisting that evening. Fort George G. Meade, twelve miles to the south, sent troops and equipment. One hundred soldiers from the Army's 35th Anti-Aircraft battalion, assigned to the half-dozen or more NIKE sites that ringed the Baltimore-Washington area to defend against a possible Soviet attack, helped keep the crowds back at the scene. They also provided first aid to a number of the injured.[41]

George Mills was working as a camera man for WJZ-TV in Baltimore. He was sent to the fire and filmed much of the action. The film was rushed back to Television Hill near Hampden in Baltimore, where it was developed and televised during special bulletins and later on the evening news. It was ultimately seen by thousands in the metropolitan area anxious to learn more about the fire.[42]

Another important contribution that night came from the Ladies Auxiliaries of the Brooklyn and Glen Burnie Fire Departments. The women, along with Baltimore City Fire Department's lunch and coffee wagon, 414, and the Salvation Army brought sandwiches, hot coffee, and other refreshments for the tired, cold, and hungry emergency workers.[43]

Approximately ten miles east of Arundel Park near the shore front community of Pasadena, Dr. Randall McLaughlin enjoyed a thriving private medical practice. Since 1949, after leaving the U.S. Army as a medical officer assigned to the dispensary at Fort George G. Meade in nearby Odenton, the Pennsylvania-born McLaughlin typically worked fifteen-hour days out of his home office on Mountain Road near the intersection with Hog Neck Road. On this cold drizzly Sunday evening, the thirty-six-year-old experienced and well-respected medical practitioner was enjoying a rare evening at home with his wife and three children when the phone rang a little after 7:00 P.M.

A ringing telephone on the weekends or in the middle of the night was not unusual for a doctor with a large practice who made many a house call.[44] He often received calls at all hours of the night from hysterical parents with small children experiencing a high fever and vomiting, or adults with severe chest pains or a bad case of the flu. But this call would be very different. Four years at the Jefferson Medical College in Philadelphia, completing the army's Specialized Training Program during World War II, and eight years of private practice had not prepared McLaughlin for what he was about to confront.

McLaughlin recognized the voice of Gustave H. "Gus" Faubert, his friend and colleague, on the other end of the line. Dr. Faubert lived and managed a respected and prosperous medical practice in Glen Burnie and also worked part-time as a deputy medical examiner for Anne Arundel County. He had just been notified by the county police of a tragic fire with numerous deaths at Arundel Park and was waiting for a police officer to pick him up and escort him to the scene. He asked McLaughlin to meet him there. Together, the two would try to identify the remains of the victims.

Though he had never attended an event at the facility, McLaughlin knew where it was and drove to the scene. After making his way through many roadblocks along Belle Grove Road, each illuminated by phosphorus flares set up by wet and tired county police officers swinging kerosene lanterns, the doctor found a place to park. At the burned out, steaming shell of what had once been Arundel Park, he met Faubert.[45]

Firefighters were placing the canvas covered victims in the back of two emergency transport vehicles. One was an ambulance/rescue unit from the Arbutus Volunteer Fire Department. The other had been provided by the Air Force. To keep the press and multitudes of sightseers away from the grim task of removing the bodies, the vehicles were backed up to the overhead door opening on the west side of the building.

With the victims secure in the backs of the large ambulances, the silent motorcade made its way to Singleton's Funeral Home on Crain Highway in Glen Burnie. McLaughlin and Faubert followed. At approximately 8:50 P.M. the motorcade arrived at Singleton's and in one of the parlor preparatory rooms the bodies were laid out for identification.[46]

Fire is technically defined as a rapid oxidation accompanied by heat and light. And with the exception of a few scientific principals that keep it alive, fire has no consciousness, and it has no soul. Fire is a non-prejudicial destroyer that attacks viciously. It has no favorites, and it is not forgiving. Whatever the fire did in its destruction of the thick wooden timbers that held up the massive roof of the Arundel Park, it emulated indiscriminately on human flesh.

Identification of the bodies was the most difficult and horrific task Doctor McLaughlin ever performed, before the fire and since. McLaughlin and Faulbert began the process while a few hand-picked county and state police officers looked on. As he worked, McLaughlin could not help but think that these lifeless victims had been only a few hours ago lovely human beings, and now they were gone forever. The scene at the funeral home would bother him and replay itself in his head for years to come.[47]

Unfortunately, the two doctors could only ascertain the gender and approximate ages of the victims. After an hour, Anne Arundel County and state police issued a joint statement to press and some family members who had gathered at the funeral home that all ten bodies were female, and three were believed to have ranged in age from six to fifteen.[48] The ages would

The Arbutus Volunteer Fire Department Rescue truck along with a large ambulance from the Air Force have backed up to the west overhead door opening as the dead are solemnly taken to be identified. (Courtesy of the Hearst Corporation.)

later prove to be wrong. Captain Martin Puenke of the Maryland State Police answered a couple of questions from reporters, then the ambulances transported the bodies to the Baltimore City morgue for a complete post mortem examination.[49]

At the morgue, Anne Arundel County Police Sergeant Elmer Hagner and Corporal Brack Testermann were given the sad task of interviewing family members of the deceased. They tried to elicit detailed personal descriptions, information on the clothing and jewelry the victims had been wearing, their ages, weights, heights, and dental and medical information.

Dr. Russell S. Fisher, state medical director, was in charge of body identification and releasing information to the next of kin. He would not allow any of the relatives to view the bodies.[50]

Eighteen-year-old Leonard Bierman, a Ferndale firefighter, carries women's shoes hurriedly kicked off during the mad rush to the exits. (Courtesy of the Hearst Corporation.)

The official identification of the dead by the Anne Arundel County Police Department was as follows:

Mrs. Goldie Otto, 8115 Liberty Road, Rockdale, age 38
Mrs. Josephine Franczkowski, 414 S. Washington Street, Baltimore, age 34
Miss Stella Kozlowski, 5627 Sagra Road, Baltimore, age 45
Mrs. Esther Daugherty, Manhattan Beach, Severna Park, age 58

Mrs. Frances Cooke, 19 Seward Avenue, Baltimore, age 48
Mrs. Anna Brandt, 3210 Foster Avenue, Baltimore, age 59
Mrs. Stella Cavanaugh, 900 Pontiac Avenue, Baltimore, age 42
Mrs. Gladys McKay, 804 Drill Court, Brooklyn, age 41
Mrs. Frances Obzut, 19 Seward Avenue, Baltimore, age 82
Mrs. Theresa Kelly, 900 Jack Street, Baltimore, age 28 [51]

On Saturday, February 4, 1956, almost one week after the fire, one of the heroes of the Arundel Park fire, Andrew Brady, died from severe burns at South Baltimore General Hospital. He was fifty-seven years old.

Witnesses said: "When the fire broke out, Brady stood on a table exhorting the panic-stricken people around him to stay calm. He remained in the hall helping people out and returned into the inferno [repeatedly], until badly burned on his face, hands, and back. Brady, a true hero, was dragged from the burning building with his uniform on fire after he had helped at least a dozen other persons to safety."[52]

Andrew Brady said on the night of the fire that he believed he was the last man out. Though he was confined to an oxygen tent during his last days, his family say that he never complained. In addition to the severe burns, Bill Brady remembers his father having a persistent case of the hiccups. He also craved ice tea which the family brought to the hospital by the gallon. Bill sat with his father during the night, and Andrew Jr. and Brady's wife Edith stayed with him during the day. On Saturday morning, as Bill was being relieved by his brother and mother, Bill told his dad to say a number of "Hail Marys" and that he would do the same thing, and maybe the hiccups would end. The Arundel Park hero replied that he had been saying them and that Bill was a "good boy" for praying for him. It would be the last time Bill Brady saw his father alive.[53]

According to his son, Andrew Jr., the elder Brady was glad to have done what he could, and God and people know what he did. Did Andrew Brady Sr. ever learn that his old company, Engine 26, had been there, fighting the fire in which he so bravely performed?[54] We will never know.

The Weather

Today—Cloudy and mild with rain ending at night, and turning much colder, highest near 48. Tuesday, partly cloudy, windy and much colder. Sunday's high, 44 at 8 p. m. low, 33 at 12:30 a. m. (Details on Page 12.)

The Washington Post and Times Herald

412,000 Sunday Circulation
381,000 Daily Circulation

79th Year — No. 56 •••• Phone RE. 7-1234 MONDAY, JANUARY 30, 1956 WTOP Radio (1500) TV (Ch. 9) FIVE CENTS

12 Killed, Hundreds Injured as Fire Sweeps Hall in Anne Arundel County

FIREMEN BATTLE THE BLAZE THAT BROKE OUT IN A PACKED HALL AT BROOKLYN PARK, MD. (OTHER PHOTOS, PAGE 15)

Scores Trampled Fleeing Blaze at Oyster Roast Attended by Over 1000

(Other Pictures on Page 15.)

At least 12 persons were killed and hundreds were injured last night when fire and resulting panic swept a church supper in Brooklyn Park, on the south edge of Baltimore in Anne Arundel County.

Police estimated that 1000 persons were present at an oyster roast and dance sponsored by the St. Rose of Lima Catholic Church at Arundel Park Hall, a quonset-type structure.

Firemen said the holocaust began when a small blaze broke out in a duct near the wooden ceiling over the kitchen. Several men climbed ladders to attempt to put it out.

"Suddenly," one eyewitness reported, "the fire shot out all along the ceiling—almost like an explosion." The crowd, which had been orderly and had been offering wisecracking advice to the firefighters, suddenly panicked.

Leo A. Rust, an oil refinery worker who attended the oyster roast with his wife and two daughters, said the fire spread "as if somebody had spread gasoline over the place."

Another survivor, Veronica Sparrow of Brooklyn Park, said: "My God, it was terrible. Women and children were knocked down and trampled."

A priest identified only as assistant pastor of the church said: "At first there was only smoke. People tried to leave in an orderly fashion. But then they saw the flames. There was some panic, and I saw people trampled."

The hall is located in the 6000 block of Belle Grove rd., about one mile south of Baltimore's city limits.

There are double doors on each side of the [illegible] building but [illegible] flames blocked the front door and eyewitnesses said there was some difficulty in getting some of the other doors open.

Al Barthelme, former coach of the Baltimore Bullets pro-

Stacked 10 Deep

[illegible] than 100 persons were treated at the scene, and that scores of others had been taken to South Baltimore General, St. Agnes, Mercy, University and Johns Hopkins Hospitals. South Baltimore General which received the greatest number of casualties, reported that it had taken in 43 casualties, [illegible] of them critically injured.

None of the victims found outside the hall were pronounced dead by Dr. Leonard H. Flax, who lives two blocks from the scene. When first survivors began making their way to his doctor's office, he [illegible] to the hall.

"Most of the dead suffocated before the flames reached them," he said. Dr. Flax treated 70 of the injured at the scene.

The fire started shortly after [illegible]

'Looked Like Pictures

There was confusion about the number of fatalities when this paper hit the streets the Monday morning after the fire. The photograph of Arundel Park, with its roof gone and flames raging throughout, appeared on front pages across the nation. (Patrick Prendergast.)

9

Accusations and Suspicion

While Andrew Brady fought for his life in South Baltimore General Hospital, and news of the disaster was spreading around the world, county police placed a twenty-four hour guard around the charred and damaged Arundel Park. Fire investigators searched the ruins for the source of the fire.

Many were asking: How had the fire started? How had it been able to spread so quickly, killing and injuring so many people? Was it just an accident, the work of a sick arsonist, or an attack by organized crime? The community demanded answers, especially the one everyone wanted to know: What could be done so this nightmare never happened again?

John Hoy was a sailor in the U.S. Navy stationed in Long Beach, California. (A volunteer with the Ferndale Volunteer Fire Company, John would later become a career firefighter with Anne Arundel County.) He remembers his shipmates receiving newspapers from their hometowns all over the country reporting the Arundel Park fire. He clipped the articles and sent them back to Willie Hubers, who was assigned to the Ferndale Station and had driven the engine the night of the fire. Nearly every paper John picked up from around the nation had run a front-page story about the tragedy at Arundel Park.[1]

The Ferndale Fire Company was only one of many organizations in the community to help during the disaster. From its small, cramped, wood-framed building with brick veneer on Baltimore & Annapolis Boulevard, the Anne Arundel County Police Department's Northern District Station had been the county's communications hub that evening.[2] With the exception of the small "POLICE" sign outside, the only things differentiating it from other businesses on the block were two large, white, light globes, mounted on either side of the station's front door.

Inside, dispatchers Warren Eyerly and veteran Sergeant Max Muller, handled the radio traffic among police crews, broadcast updated information over the air, and answered a rash of phone calls from worried relatives and friends. Desperate for news of their loved ones, many actually showed up at the station. In addition to calls from across North County and Baltimore City, the dispatchers received calls from news agencies around the world. At approximately 7:45 P.M., a "transoceanic call" came in from the *London Times* requesting the latest on the death toll. The dispatchers told the *Times* to call back later—the information was not yet available.[3]

Calls came in from people who wanted to help in any way they could. Eyerly and Muller found and coordinated transportation for the hundreds who offered to donate blood and who subsequently were sent to various hospitals. Other calls came in from people who wanted to send sandwiches and hot drinks to the fire, police, and ambulance crews working that long night. The volunteers were told where to go and who to see since police had closed down Belle Grove Road from 5th Avenue to Thomas Avenue.

With all of the chaos, tragedy, and confusion that evening, the dispatchers took one memorable phone call from a couple who had escaped the fire. They had left the scene and were calling the police station to report that someone had stolen the woman's pocketbook. They wanted to know what the police were going to do about it.[4]

The next week saw newspapers filled with articles on Baltimore. Local papers published any number of editorials and "sidewalk surveys" taken by roaming news reporters. A *Washington Post* editorial wondered, "Where was the Fire Marshal?"[5] The *New York Times* on Monday published a front-page article under the headline, "10 Die, 228 Hurt as Hall Burns in Baltimore."

But the Arundel Park fire had to share the national spotlight with another story out of Baltimore that Monday. Sometime between the hour he retired on Saturday evening and the first mass at Saint Rose of Lima on Sunday

Taken from the northeast side of the front of the building, this photo shows coats and other clothing removed from the "Cloak Room," piled by fire fighters, and carefully soaked. Note the casement windows and the small opening created when the center sash was pushed out. (Lorretta Kane Dove.)

morning, January 29, author, editor, and newspaperman H. L Mencken, died at his Hollins Street home in Baltimore at the age of seventy-five. The famed critic of the American scene was an iconic figure, hated by some and beloved by many more. National newspapers gave more ink to Mencken's biography and obituary than to the deadly fire.

Not so in Baltimore, where shock was followed by questions that grew more stern as time passed. "The fire scene will remain seared in spectator's minds — a scene of pushing, screaming and shoving; a scene [of] men and women bereft of their self control . . . a horrible, blackened tragedy," the *Baltimore Sun* observed on Monday. Then it continued in a different vein: "The fire code and inspection system in Anne Arundel County need careful review. The dead cannot be helped by getting at the facts, but people in

Flaming Death

THE FLASH fire and panic which cost the lives of ten women and injuries to 250 persons is one of the most shocking catastrophies of Baltimore's history.

It demands, and undoubtedly will get, searching investigation, out of which must grow more rigid precautions against such tragedies.

With all the facts not yet known, there is no intention here to attach blame. We are told that the building, with its adjacent structures, had been inspected by the Fire Prevention Bureau of Anne Arundel county during the past month.

Evidently it passed muster of the inspectors, since public gatherings were permitted to continue in it.

But the tragedy re-emphasizes how thorough must be, in general, the inspection and regulation of structures where crowds congregate.

We are reminded of the Cocoanut Grove night club fire which killed 491 in Boston; the St. Ambrose hall blaze in which eight died, and the fire in a Baltimore street business structure which caused the deaths of six fire fighters.

The Cocoanut Grove holocaust was taken to heart by Baltimore's building inspection forces. Local night clubs which had inadequate escape facilities were required to build additional exits and install other safety measures.

Accounts of the oyster roast fire indicate that the nearest fire plug was blocked to fire fighters by parked autos. This shows tragically bad judgment on the part of the motorists and indicates how strict and watchful police must be in enforcing the law.

Also, the throng of morbidly curious who surrounded the scene, hampering the emergency work of fire fighters, ambulance crews and police, constitutes a usual but unfortunate phenomenon at fires. Persons who have no loved ones involved should restrain their curiosity and stay at a distance.

Many firetrap structures still exist in and near Baltimore. Even some hospitals fall in that category, although precautions against fire disaster are extremely rigid in them.

Our authorities with supervision over buildings should learn an added lesson from the Sunday tragedy.

Eternal vigilance is the price of safety.

We extend our sincere sympathy to the relatives of the dead and to the injured.

crowded halls everywhere can be helped, if authorities can learn what steps may prevent a second disaster."[6]

Two days after the fire, on Tuesday, January 31, the *News-Post* printed an editorial under the title, "Flaming Death." The fire, it said, "is one of the most shocking catastrophes in Baltimore history. It demands and undoubtedly will get searching investigation, out of which must grow more rigid precautions against such tragedies." The editorial went on to admonish the motorist who had used tragically bad judgment in parking in front of the fire hydrant, and the throng of morbidly curious onlookers who had surrounded the scene, thereby hampering the emergency work of firefighters, ambulance crews, and police. It continued: "Our authorities with supervision over buildings should learn an added lesson from the Sunday tragedy. Eternal vigilance is the price of safety. We extend our sincere sympathy to the relatives of the dead and to the injured."[7]

On Thursday the *News-Post* commended the South Baltimore General Hospital organization for the magnificent role it played in dealing with the sudden flood of burned and injured from Arundel Park. In addition to the 120 fire-related cases, the emergency room had handled another seventy-five cases that day in varying degrees of urgency. Yet when the Arundel Park casualties came in, "Order was established quickly among hysterical victims and relatives, off-duty doctors and nurses hurried to the hospital, and the entire staff from Director Donald T. Mills down worked around the clock. No doubt they saved many lives. No victim was turned away." It should also be noted that on the crossword page of Wednesday night's edition of the *News-Post* someone had been awarded fifty dollars for the news tip alerting the newsroom of the fatal fire.[8]

Also on Thursday, the *Maryland Gazette*, a weekly newspaper focusing on local events, ran a front-page editorial expressing shock and sadness and extending its deepest sympathy to those who had lost loved ones. The paper also commended the work of the firefighters, police officers, ambulance crews, physicians, and nurses on the scene and at the hospitals as well as the Red Cross.[9] It then urged a thorough review of all county regulations dealing with fire prevention in the county's public assemblies to prevent future tragedies.

Opposite: Baltimore News-Post *article, "Flaming Death." (Patrick Prendergast.)*

Pictures Ads | Maryland Gazette — WEEKLY — GLEN BURNIE NEWS | This Week

VOL. CCXXVII NO. 5—Two Sections, 32 Pages — GLEN BURNIE, MD., THURSDAY, FEBRUARY 2, 1956 — PRICE TEN CENTS

OUTSIDE BLAZE HAD BEEN FOUND 20 MINUTES BEFORE INDOOR FIRE

EDITORIAL

The people of Anne Arundel County, of Maryland, and of the nation as well, were shocked and saddened by the tragic loss of life Sunday in the Arundel Park oyster roast fire.

Striking suddenly, the fire and ensuing panic turned a social and happy occasion into a scene of terror and horror, leaving 10 women dead in its wake.

We know we can speak for the people of Anne Arundel in expressing the deepest sympathy to those who lost loved ones in the tragedy. We also realize that this fails to ease the sorrow of loss, but we can only say that this sympathy comes from the heart.

From time to time we read of disasters in other parts of the nation with shock and sadness. Now we realize that it can happen here, bringing with it the loss of friends and acquaintances and the disruption of family circles.

It is the second time within a six-month period that there has been a major disaster in the local area, involving death to groups who previously had been enjoying themselves. It was on August 14 that the vacation cruise schooner Levin J. Marvel broke up in the Chesapeake Bay, off North Beach, with the loss of 14 lives. The Marvel rolled over in the rough seas which preceded Hurricane Connie.

The investigation into the Arundel Park fire has been started and judging from the statements of county officials it will be thorough. Ralph J. Lowman, president of the Board of Anne Arundel County Commissioners, has stated that the county officials will not "jump to conclusions" and "will be in no position to reach any decisions until completion of the multiple investigations now under way."

Three county agencies—the County Police, the Department of Building Inspection and the Bureau of Fire Prevention—along

THE DAY AFTER—This is the scene that Gazette-News photographer recorded Monday morning at 10:15 when he went back to the scene of the tragic Arundel Park fire of the evening before. Combing the wreckage of the razed structure are members of the arson squad.

List Of Dead

'Worst Nightmare Imaginable'

Jack Everd Credited With Saving Lives

Behind Scenes:

Communications Prove Vital In Sunday Disaster

By E. M. JACKSON III

New Probe Discloses Breakout

Probability Of Shock Had Deterred Men In First Try At Fire

(Other Photos & Stories, Page 27)

By E. M. JACKSON III

Anne Arundel County Police definitely established late last night (Wednesday) that fire was discovered on the outside of the Arundel Park Auditorium Sunday at least 20 minutes before the blaze inside was found.

The Maryland Gazette ran a front-page editorial on the fire expressing the paper's shock at the loss of life and extending its sympathy to those who had lost loved ones. (Patrick Prendergast.)

Reporters conducting "sidewalk surveys" asked passers-by, "What can be done to prevent disastrous fires in public places?" The answers were more exits, exit signs, improved evacuation instructions, increased fire inspections, smoking bans, and the installation of automatic sprinkler systems.[10]

IN THE WAKE OF THE TRAGEDY questions arose regarding fire safety in public assemblies. Government officials called for special meetings to discuss what action should be taken to prevent such fires from ever happening again. On Monday, less than twenty-four hours from the start of the Arundel Park fire, the Anne Arundel County commissioners convened in a special meeting. Presiding officer Ralph L. Lowman explained that, although they would discuss the incident at Tuesday's regularly scheduled meeting, they would not be able to reach a decision until all of the investigations had been completed.[11]

Lowman did say that, based on what he had gleaned from preliminary reports, "Panic was a key factor in the loss of life" and that "all the safeguards in the world won't do much good when you've got a thousand people in panic."[12] In a *News-Post* article published on Wednesday, February 1, Lowman added: "About a month before the fire, the Arundel Park's insurance carrier conducted an inspection of the facility that thoroughly examined the building and found it safe and acceptable reducing its fire insurance rate."[13]

Other jurisdictions in the Baltimore-Washington corridor decided to reevaluate their fire regulations. According to the *News-Post*, Prince George's and Montgomery Counties both ordered crackdowns to enforce fire safety regulations in public assembly halls.[14] The Baltimore City Fire Commissioners called a special meeting to determine if they should write stricter fire codes for the city's many places of public assembly.

According to the newspapers, Senator Phillip H. Goodman, a Democrat from the city's Fifth Council District, wrote a letter to city council president Leon Abramson to request tougher fire codes for public assemblies such as roasts and other large gatherings. He also requested a greater police presence at these events.[15] Goodman proposed a city ordinance requiring fire and police presence at all public assembly events of five hundred people or more. Establishments holding those events would have to obtain a permit. Police and fire inspectors assigned to them would be required to continuously check exit door operation and hazardous decorations, and to maintain order in the event a fire or similar emergency occurred.[16]

The Baltimore County Fire Department's chief fire marshal, Louis C. Maisel, announced a departmental survey of all church and public assembly halls in the county. "All assembly halls that typically hold oyster roasts and bingo will get special attention." Maisel ordered that an announcement be made at the start of these functions to have patrons check the location of the nearest fire exit. He also initiated the practice of having members of his fire prevention staff attend oyster roasts and bingo affairs.[17]

Leo H. McCormick, the one-time World War II OPA director, asked that Governor Theodore McKeldin appoint the state attorney general to the board investigating the Arundel Park fire. According to news reports, McCormick told the governor, "It is your job as the leader of the State to represent each small individual right in this [tragedy] . . . this [is] the greatest catastrophe that has ever happened in my lifetime."[18]

Chief Wilbur C. Wade of the Anne Arundel County Police had been head of the department a little less than a year when the fire occurred. Here he stands in the door of the new mobile police lab in 1960 with his staff. From left to right: Elmer Hagner, Captain Edward King, Captain George Wellham and Sergeant Clyde Graham. (Courtesy of the Hearst Corporation.)

Rumors of how the fire started and grew so quickly spread through the community like a summer flash flood. "Facts" became clouded, and contradictory reports added to the confusion and controversy. The public and the media were looking for someone or something to blame for the ten deaths. Accusations were quickly addressed as investigators tackled every possible lead and examined every shred of evidence.

Wilbur C Wade, chief of the Anne Arundel County Police Department, believed there had been two fires at Arundel Park, one in the kitchen and a second in the main hall. Wade, who possessed a sterling record in law enforcement, had only been Anne Arundel County's police chief for a little less than a year. Interviewed on Monday, the day after the fire, Wade told Roy Gregory of the *New-Post* that he had attended many functions at Arundel Park over the years and could not understand how the fire burned so quickly and completely. "Actually there wasn't much there to really burn," he said. "Indications from where the bodies were found make it seem as if they were crushed in the corner of the building probably during the height of the panic." The much decorated veteran police officer continued: "This is the worst that I have experienced. Everything happened so quickly. It is the worst disaster to strike in Anne Arundel County to my knowledge and I've been in the county all of my life."[19]

The police did not rule out arson. The *News-Post* also quoted an unnamed arson expert as saying, "Since the fire shot across the ceiling along two distinct fire lines, a trailer incendiary device may have been used since it would have left such lines." He added, "A trailer bomb is composed of an igniter and two long strips of paper treated with highly inflammable material. Adding machine paper rolls are often used for these trailers."[20]

Chief Wade reported, "Some witnesses have been reluctant to talk about the fire," and further, some had been "un-cooperative." He added: "We shall continue to question witnesses today [Monday] and until we have a clear answer as to the real cause of the fire, we shall continue to guard the ruins to preserve all of the evidence."[21]

According to one rumor, a Baltimore Gas and Electric Company trouble crew had been sent to the complex to investigate a reported gas leak on the morning of that fateful Sunday, but a company spokesperson said there was no evidence of the call. Another rumor claimed that leaking gas from one of the ceiling heating units had ignited, touching off the deadly blaze.[22] A report that a similar fire had occurred at Arundel Park in December 1955 was quickly quashed by the Brooklyn Fire Department, which claimed that they had not responded to a fire at Arundel Park since 1954, and that one had started in the electrical system.[23]

Inconsistencies also appeared in the statements survivors made regarding the park's overhead doors. As patrons tried to escape, one of the overhead doors may have been raised, then lowered again. John Miles Jr. and his friend Wayne MocGogg had been standing by a bar near the kitchen when the fire was first discovered above and around the ceiling trap door. When the flames roared across the ceiling, people began screaming, and both men headed for the nearest exit. John said the overhead door was only opened part way, then lowered.

Unable to get out through the overhead door, Miles and MocGogg had then run for the front door. According to Miles, "The crowd was shoving and screaming and women went down. I stepped on someone on the floor, and reached down and tried to help a woman to her feet but I was carried away with the crowd and lost my grip on her. The whole place went up in a matter of minutes. I believe everyone could have got out if they would have left the door open part of the way."[24]

The probe into the fire's origin widened as the county's building, and fire prevention agencies joined in with the police. A task force of agency representatives spent most of Monday, January 30, going through the ruins. Other organizations—the state fire commission, state police and the fire underwriters—were conducting their own investigations.

The county building inspector, John H. Hevener, reported that his department had inspected the building in December 1955 and found it to be in perfectly good condition. According to Hevener, Arundel Park's seven exits met the fire regulations. Hevener also told investigators, "There was no indication of excessive overcrowding in the hall." County regulations required ten square feet per person. At 12,800 square feet, the hall would have accommodated 1,280 people safely, he concluded.[25]

About a week after the fire, the Fire Prevention Committee of the Anne Arundel County Volunteer Firemen's Association met with the chairman of the county commissioners, Ralph Lowman, and requested that another inspector be hired at a salary of $4,100 per year to assist Harry Klasmeier in the fire marshal's office. John Smith of the West Annapolis Fire Department and a member of the advisory committee noted, "Klasmeier was the only employee in the bureau," and his workload had increased tremendously as a direct result of the Arundel Park disaster. Since the fire, the fire marshal's office had been flooded with requests for inspections of amusement centers and community beach resorts. Lowman downplayed the requests and argued that a second inspector would not have averted the holocaust.[26]

In the 1950s, crime, political corruption, and gambling were not strangers to Anne Arundel County. On February 1, the *Baltimore Sun* stated that the county police department was investigating the possibility that the fire had been "criminally inspired."[27] There were a number of good reasons to pursue a possible criminal angle. In the 1950s only a few jurisdictions in the United States sponsored legalized gambling—the State of Nevada and the southern Maryland counties of Anne Arundel, Calvert, Charles and Saint Mary's.[28]

In Anne Arundel County, pinball machines and slot machines or "one-armed bandits" were available almost everywhere. The county itself was known as "Little Nevada," and it was said that there were more slot machines in southern Maryland than in that entire state.[29] One could not enter a lunchroom, diner, gas station, drug store, restaurant, beach resort, grocery store, bowling alley, bingo parlor, or tavern without hearing the chrome steel balls of a pinball machine setting off bells and whistles or hearing quarters jingling down into the money tray of a one-armed bandit.[30] In "Little Nevada" slot machines were a fact of life. Even the fire stations had them. Arundel Park was known to have had an entire wall full of slots.

"Little Nevada" was not the only unofficial title bestowed upon Anne Arundel County. Prior to its receiving a charter in 1965, the county had also been referred to as the "Banana Republic." This unflattering designation was largely due to the board of county commissioners' loose management style and their appointment of political hacks to departmental positions.[31]

Like most Maryland counties at the time, a board of commissioners headed Anne Arundel County's government. Corruption was rumored to exist within the commission, which consisted of eight elected board members. Businessman recalled that "getting permits to build or expand was difficult, if not impossible, without passing money to the right person."[32] The board of the "Banana Republic" became largely dysfunctional as the county's growth spun out of control. Political patronage flourished. No merit system protected employees. Commissioners hired and fired at will.[33]

In the mid-1940s, when the four southern Maryland counties legalized gambling, Anne Arundel County's board of commissioners granted eleven licenses for slot machines. Despite the fact that gambling yielded "tremendous profits," not one cent went into the county coffers. Not one dime of slot machine receipts was spent on education, police and fire protection, or public works projects. It was rumored that profits that could have supported the local economy were used instead to influence elected officials. Other rumors

Slot machines could be found everywhere in Anne Arundel County. These machines were located in the Sanitary Food Market on Ritchie Highway, a block north of the Brooklyn Volunteer Fire Department station. Photograph taken in 1961. (Courtesy of the Hearst Corporation.)

claimed that every Monday morning cars full of coins left Anne Arundel County for Jersey City.[34]

Businessmen who refused to permit slot machines in their establishments were often threatened by affiliates of the eleven licensees. These affiliates were also known as the "syndicate."[35] According to an article in the *Arundel Observer* in 1959, the slots profits were estimated at approximately fifty million dollars annually. The Anne Arundel County Grand Jury flatly stated in 1958 that the "syndicate" spent at least $50,000 on candidates who could vote to keep them—the syndicate—in business.[36]

Fires of uncertain origin occurred at some restaurants and taverns in North County. One tavern owner was threatened with harm to his pregnant wife if he refused to install the machines. Needless to say, he installed them.[37] In 1955 the county police were called to investigate an attempted dynamite bombing of the "Forty-Niner" bingo parlor, on Church and 6th Streets in Brooklyn Park. The police probe found that many businesses in the county had been approached by criminal groups to share in the profits

U.S. Marshal Gerald F. Bracken looks on as FBI agents load confiscated illegal slot machines into a truck in southern Maryland in 1955. (Courtesy of the Hearst Corporation.)

Anne Arundel County police burn confiscated slot machines at the dump at the end of Dover Road near Ritchie Highway in Glen Burnie, Maryland, in the early 1960s. (Courtesy of the Hearst Corporation.)

of slot machines and bingo. There were also reports that mobsters had been trying to muscle in on the lucrative county slots operations.

So it did not come as a surprise when the *News-Post* hit the streets on February 1 with an article proclaiming: "Mafia Plot Eyed in Fire." The article explained that "In view of past attempts by criminal elements—identified sometimes as the Mafia, or Italian Black Hand society—to infiltrate slot-machines and bingo organizations in the county, authorities are anxious to run down the origin of the fire."[38] One theory was that an incendiary device or bomb had been covertly installed and set to go off during the previous Saturday night's bingo games, but because of faulty workmanship the device

A slot machine, with its lower access panel opened, still rests against the lavatory wall of the milk bar, which is just to the left of the brick column on the right. A destroyed cigarette vending machine and ceiling mounted gas heater lie scorched and mangled near the exit-way though which hundreds fled once the double doors placed in this opening were broken open. Thoughtlessly, they had been left padlocked. (Lorretta Kane Dove.)

did not detonate until the next day, triggering the fatal fire. The police investigation suggested a threat from the "Mafia," whose bid to become a part of Arundel Park's bingo operation had been turned down.[39] According to police, Roy Helms, part owner of the Arundel Park Corporation, had been approached by organized crime and had refused to listen to their proposal. As a result of these criminal allegations, H. Charles Robertson, a special investigator for the county police who was currently assigned to undercover work on county gambling, was attached to the fire investigation team by

Looking north toward where the I-895 Bridge is today. At far left, Belle Grove Road rises in elevation to 6th Avenue. The white structure in the background is the Matlack Trucking Company. (Lorretta Kane Dove.)

Chief Wilbur Wade. Roberson's charge was to rule out the possibility that the fire was tied to the Mafia.[40]

While the task force of government agencies was painstakingly trying to determine the cause of the Brooklyn fire, in the state capital thirty miles to the south senators and delegates were writing a special resolution to honor a true hero of the fire. On Monday, February 6, 1956, members of the Maryland House of Delegates stood respectfully and adopted a resolution "Expressing the deepest sympathy of the House over the passing of Andrew A. Brady, Sr., a beloved person to Anne Arundel Countians and Baltimoreans who have attended oyster roasts and other church functions in the county and who died as the result of burns suffered in the Arundel Park fire. . . . Six days

Andrew Brady Sr. at the wedding of his daughter, Nancy, in June 1954. (Courtesy of Nancy Brady Thompson.)

House Resolution

No. 6

MR. LUBER and ANNE ARUNDEL COUNTY DELEGATION

By the HOUSE OF DELEGATES, February 6, 1956.

[I]ntroduced, read the first time, rules suspended and adopted.

By order, GEORGE W. OWINGS, JR., Chief Clerk.

House Resolution expressing the deepest sympathy of the House of Delegates over the passing of Andrew Brady.

1 On February 5, 1956, Andrew Brady, long a beloved person to
2 Anne Arundel Countians and Baltimoreans who have attended oyster
3 roasts and other such functions in the County, died as a result of
4 burns suffered in the disastrous fire at Arundel Park;

5 Mr. Brady had been a member of the Baltimore City Fire Depart-
6 ment since joining the Department in January 1921, until his retire-
7 ment from the Force in 1943. He was an assistant engine man for
8 Engine Company No. 26, at the time of his retirement, and had spent
9 all but two years of his service with the Fire Department in South
10 Baltimore;

11 Andrew Brady was a school crossing guard, a familiar sight on
12 the Ritchie Highway to the students of Brooklyn Park High School;

13 Eighteen months ago, Mr. Brady was sworn in as a special police-
14 man in Anne Arundel County, and was attending the oyster roast
15 sponsored by St. Rose of Lima Parish of which he was a member, at
16 Arundel Park in his capacity as a special policeman;

17 As the fire broke out in the Hall at Arundel Park, Andrew Brady
18 stood on a table exhorting the panic-stricken people around him to
19 stay calm. He remained in the hall, helping people out and returning
20 into the inferno until badly burned about the hands, face and back.
21 Mr. Brady said in the hospital "I think I was the last man out."

22 Six days after the fire occurred, Andrew Brady paid with his life
23 for his utter courageousness and extreme self-sacrifice for the safety
24 of his fellow men; now therefore be it

25 *Resolved that the House of Delegates of Maryland* expresses its
26 deepest sympathies over the untimely passing of Andrew Brady, and
27 be it further

28 *Resolved*, That the Chief Clerk of the House of Delegates be in-
29 structed to send a suitable copy of this Resolution to the family of
30 Andrew Brady, Brooklyn, Maryland.

after the fire [February 4], Brady paid with his life for his utter courageousness and extreme self-sacrifice for the safety of his fellow man."

House Speaker John C. Luber and the Anne Arundel County delegation introduced the resolution. When it was read, "Delegate Ira Bird Kirkland, chairman of the county delegation, moved that the rules be suspended and the resolution be adopted at once."[41]

Sifting through the ruins near the kitchen serving window are, from left to right: Anne Arundel County Police Special Investigator H. Charles Robertson, Detective Charles F. Gleim, and Maryland State Police Detective Sergeant Thomas Smith. (Courtesy of the Hearst Corporation.)

10

"I Solved These Firebug Mysteries"

On Monday morning, January 30, the sun rose on what was left of Arundel Park. Investigators could now let the fire companies' "enginemen" shut down the overheated generators powering the numerous utility lights that had illuminated the first search operations and were still scattered haphazardly around the building's burned-out shell. Flashlights and hand lanterns, already dim from working through the night, could be switched off. For the firefighters, police, and investigators still at the scene, the morning light made the devastation look all the worse.

A detective in a light gray overcoat, white shirt, and necktie still neatly in place stood in what was left of Arundel Park's roofless kitchen. Thomas Smith of the Maryland State Police was an experienced investigator. The Eastern Shore native was in his fifteenth year with Maryland's elite law enforcement agency. In 1951, Smith had been assigned to work with the U.S. Senate committee handling the famous Kefauver probe into America's organized crime.[1] He would prove to be an asset to the investigation and was eventually promoted to state police superintendent, where he served three different Maryland governors from 1970 to 1982.[2]

On this Monday morning, Detective Smith squatted down in the ash and debris on the kitchen floor, slowly so as not to soil his clothes, and raised

Discarded clothing offers mute evidence of the panic. Note the metal casement windows broken out in the frenzied attempt to escape the flames. (Unidentified photograph courtesy of Patrick Prendergast.)

the brim of his hat for a better view. With a small metal scoop, he dug into the charred rubble and brought up chunks of charred wood that he carefully dropped into a clean metal container about the size of a pint can of paint.[3] He stood up and placed the container on the soot-covered gas cooking range, the knobs of which had been burned off. He sealed it, attached a label, and marked it "Kitchen." Smith repeated this ritual a number of times as he picked up specimens of carbonized debris from all parts of the hall. The specimens would be hand-carried to forensic laboratories for examination.[4] Detective Smith personally saw to it that the containers, along with other pieces of equipment now considered "evidence"—fan motors, neon light transformers, electrical switchboxes, and cut-out sections of the building's heavy wooden frame—followed established "chain of custody" protocol. That process ensures that when evidence is secured, transported, and tested it always remains under the control of the investigating agency.[5]

At the laboratory certified specialists and technicians would test the charred wood for the presence of flammable liquids, even traces of which could indicate arson. The electrical equipment would be checked for short circuits and, if any were found, to determine whether they occurred before the fire, possibly starting it, or as a result of the fire. All of these tests were intended to determine whether the fire was accidental or the result of malicious activity.[6]

Anne Arundel County was in the initial stages of the most important and comprehensive investigation ever conducted within its jurisdiction. The county commissioners selected a four-man committee to first determine how the fire started and then learn why the ten victims had been unable to escape.[7] They selected Chief Fire Marshal Harry Klasmeier to head the investigation.[8] He would be aided by Detective Smith of the state police, Detective Charles F. Gleim of the Anne Arundel County police, and H. Charles Robertson, a special investigator who had been hired as a consultant by the county police. Representatives of local, state, and national organizations offered assistance and volunteered their services:

Chief Wilber Wade, Anne Arundel County Police Department;
R. B Spencer, Special Agent of the Board of Fire Underwriters;
John Havener, Chief Building Inspector, Anne Arundel County;
Richard E. Stevens, National Fire Protection Association;
Chief Louis L. Maisel, Baltimore County Fire Prevention Bureau;
Chief Joseph Niel, Brooklyn Volunteer Fire Department;
Lieutenant D. Broke, Fort George G. Meade;
Sergeant Elmer Hagner, Anne Arundel County Police Department;
William Miller, Electrical Construction Division, Board of Fire Underwriters.

The investigators expected to question all of the witnesses in order to gather as much information as possible about what had gone on inside the hall before and during the fire, and what had taken place outside after it.[9] Their first step would be to obtain a set of plans of the Arundel Park facility in order to review and study the physical layout of the building and build a scale model of it. Witnesses could then point out where they had been relative to the rows of tables and chairs and the exit doors, and where they were during any actions they described. That way investigators could more accurately determine what the witnesses had seen at every stage of the fire.

Unfortunately, the building plans were never found and the model never built.[10] Arundel Park's architects, Kubitz and Koenig, were both deceased, and the only surviving set of plans had been lost in the fire. Instead of a model, a two-dimensional floor and seating plan was drawn to scale on a large four-foot-square display board.[11] Information for the display board was obtained in discussions with officers of the Arundel Park Corporation and by making actual measurements of the building's remains. By field inspection the committee obtained the building's overall dimensions, the location of the interior walls and wall openings, positions of tables and chairs, the exact location of the bandstand, and the placement of the exit doors. Klasmeier told the newspapers, "The probe would take some time, but now time is no element."[12]

To reconstruct individual actions and determine what witnesses had seen, the investigators asked them to describe their movements and responses verbally and, if possible, recreate them physically. In so doing they hoped to elicit more information about the sequence of events that had led to the panic, injuries, and deaths. Witnesses were interviewed wherever it was convenient for them. They were questioned at home, at the burned-out shell of the park, or at the Ferndale police station. Most of the interviews were conducted by Detective Gleim and Special Investigator Robertson.[13]

Investigators also viewed the film clip that Ralph Yenger had taken during the fire's first stages. Yenger, a member of the Brooklyn Volunteer Fire Department who had been standing northwest of the structure along Belle Grove Road, offered his film to the investigating committee. Though only two minutes long and slightly underexposed, it vividly shows the fire's tremendous power and volume as it roared across the interior and broke through each end of the massive structure.[14]

Although the investigators initially had wanted to interview most of the 1,200 people who had attended the oyster roast, after a number of discussions they decided five hundred was a more realistic number. Many of the survivors, though, opted not to talk about the most frightful five minutes of their lives. Only seventy-six of those asked agreed to be interviewed.[15]

As far as the Anne Arundel County government was concerned, this incident was a huge "hot potato" and the commissioners were not going to leave anything to chance. A special committee of Anne Arundel's sitting grand jury was requested to make its own complete and comprehensive investigation independent of Klasmeier's. Wilfred T. Azar and Henry G.

A frame from Yenger's color film taken during the fire. The huge Quonset roof is barely visible on the western edge (right side) over the last window near the telephone pole. (Ralph Yenger.)

Wever, both of Annapolis, were assigned to the grand jury committee. Grand jury foreman Edward S. Corcoran requested that the special committee characterize their investigation as a follow-up in the public interest and designated Azar as the chairman.[16]

Anticipating legal action against them, the owners of the Arundel Park Corporation promptly retained the services of "Fire Investigation, Inc.," a New York private investigation firm, to conduct their own probe of the disaster.[17] The man they hired, Thomas Patrick Brophy, was known nationally as one of the foremost experts in the investigation of fires.[18]

Brophy had gained an extensive background in this sort of work by the time he retired as chief fire marshal of the New York City Fire Department in 1949. He had been hired as an investigator for New York in 1907, only a few years after the Great Baltimore Fire. During his forty-two-year career with the city, Brophy claimed to have investigated more than 100,000 fires. As fire marshal, he had trapped, arrested, and obtained the conviction of more incendiaries than any other public official in the U.S.[19]

In February 1942, two months after the United States entered World War II, Brophy investigated the infamous *Normandie* fire in New York's Hudson River shipyard. The *Normandie* was a luxury ocean liner being converted to a troop ship, and the five-alarm fire triggered fears of espionage and sabotage. Those rumors were still flying across the world's radio waves and press reports when Brophy solved the mystery. He had arrived during the fire's early stages and begun interviewing the shipyard workers. He learned that the fire had started when sparks from a welder's torch touched off a fire that quickly spread to more than 1,100 combustible bales of kapok life preservers.[20]

In February 1956, Thomas Brophy, the "world renowned" fire investigator, now seventy-six, and an assistant named Abe Bernhardt, a former lieutenant in the New York City Fire Department, traveled down to Brooklyn, Maryland, to investigate and report on the Arundel Park fire. The pair spent from noon February 3 until the evening of February 11, repeatedly going over the site, taking pictures, and speaking with witnesses and other investigators.[21]

When completed, Brophy's eighteen-page report was every bit as professional and comprehensive as the county and the National Fire Protection Association (NFPA) reports. Generally it also contained much the same information, although it focused more on the details of the building's construction and the technical operation and location of its mechanical devices. Brophy offered no startling new theory or evidence to explain the fire and the ensuing panic. Although his report included information not revealed in the county report, it supported similar conclusions.

Brophy went to great lengths explaining the operation and basic mechanics of Arundel Park's electrical and air-conditioning/ventilation systems. He thoroughly examined the building's construction and seconded the presence of the highly combustible celotex ceiling panels, which contributed greatly to the smoke and the fire's rapid spread.[22] He further detailed the construction of the brick fireplace and chimney outside the kitchen where the oysters

I Solved These Firebug Mysteries

By THOMAS PATRICK BROPHY

Chief Fire Marshal, City of New York, Retired

One of the deadliest menaces to closely built cities is the pyromaniac, a person with a recurrent compulsion to start fires. An arson detective who dealt with many of them takes you inside the twisted minds of these psychopaths.

CONCLUSION

THE pyromaniacs are a strange bunch. These are twisted people who become so fascinated by fire that they cannot resist a periodic impulse to set one. They set them in cellars, unoccupied buildings, lumberyards or rubbish piles and, to a lesser extent, hospitals, hotels and churches.

I don't know what the big attraction of empty baby carriages is, except that they are usually parked in tenement hallways and make a handy fire basket, but the pyros sure like them. I've had some big arguments with tenants about keeping these fire hazards out of the halls.

One of the closest shaves I ever had was while investigating a series of three baby-carriage fires a few years ago in Williamsburg, an old tenement section of Brooklyn. A Lithuanian woman mistook me for the firebug and chased me with a carving knife.

I had gone into the rear courtyard of a tenement. The yard was divided by a high fence covered with vines, and was crowded with screaming women and children. I didn't have a chance to explain who I was. I just went tearing for that fence with my assailant right behind me, jabbing that knife. So I made what was probably the highest jump on record in the Fire Department, and escaped by a hair.

The pyromaniacs—unlike the torches who set fires for profit—are always with us. I estimate that there are 400 known

LARRY KEIGHLEY

Peering from a charred Brooklyn doorway, Brophy makes notes which may trace the fire's origin.

Arundel Park's owners hired world renowned fire investigator Thomas Brophy to conduct an extensive investigation of the fire. (Photograph by Larry Keighley. Courtesy, Lorretta Kane Dove.)

were roasted. To this day, Harry Klasmeier still believes that the fire may have been caused by a defective flue lining in that chimney.

According to the Brophy report, bingo operations on Saturday, January 28, concluded at 11:30 A.M., at which time the entire building was cleaned. A fire starting late in the evening or early in the morning in all likelihood would have been discovered by the cleaning crew.[23] In Brophy's opinion, atmospheric conditions such as high humidity, rain, fog, and poor visibility may have hampered early discovery. He further believed that the heavy outside air may have interfered with normal ventilation and prevented the smoke from escaping the attic and being detected outside.

Brophy's observations point to the existence of problems with the electrical system long before the fire actually broke out. According to his report, Roy Helms arrived at the facility at approximately 4:15 on Sunday afternoon. He first noticed that the outside neon lights were off. On entering

Inside the hall looking east toward the kitchen. The trap door that Leroy Helms opened was on the ceiling between the kitchen doorway in the center and the large opening of the overhead door to the left. (Gary Utz.)

the building he confronted Bob Middlekrauf about the problem, and Bob replied that he had switched on the lights moments earlier. Brophy's report also states that when the first attempts were made to extinguish the fire in the kitchen ceiling, the neon lights on the exterior wall were flickering.[24]

As was the case with the county report, Brophy believed that a backdraft occurred when the ceiling trap door in the main hall and the east side large overhead doors were opened simultaneously. He supported that opinion by pointing to a series of events. While Roy Helms was climbing the ladder and opening the trap door on the east side of the building, William Helms (possibly Roy's nephew), the manager of the cocktail lounge, noticed smoke in the corridor between the lounge and the lounge kitchen. At first, William thought it was only cigarette smoke. Moments later, as the smoke became heavier and moved downward from the ceiling, he decided to investigate. When he opened a ceiling trap door in the lounge, he saw heavy smoke, replaced the door, and shouted to a patron, "Call the fire department!"[25]

In the absence of any emergency plan, William acted on his own. Instead of unlocking the door between the lounge and the main hall and investigating further, which might have alerted others to the problem, he ran out of the building in search of his mother. She was attending the affair, and the quickest way to find her was from the outside. William ran along the south side of the hall and the exterior of the kitchen. In his interview with Brophy, he said he was so excited he never noticed the attempts being made to extinguish the fire at the kitchen, nor did he see any smoke or fire. He turned the corner and continued running along the east side, where he did notice someone breaking out a window with a chair. William finally entered the office at the front of the building just as a flash occurred and the lights went out. Fortunately for the Helms family, many of whom were in attendance, all escaped with at most minor injuries.

Theodore Heying, a Baltimore City firefighter assigned to Truck 6, South Hanover Street, was helping to look for the source of the smoke in the cocktail lounge as William Helms ran out of it. Heying was trying to remove the trap door cover a second time when he heard a rumbling noise. He ran outside and saw flames on the roof near the kitchen.

Many others heard noises just before the fire flashed out over the hall's ceiling. Domenic Kazubinski not only saw the neon lights flickering but heard a rumble or a small explosion when the large eastside overhead door was opened. Michael Jezierski said, "It was a 'puff' and a flash.'" Carroll Morgan, outside walking along the south side of the building, was attracted by a slight disturbance. As he saw smoke coming down from the ceiling, he heard a rumble.[26]

Rumblings, disturbances, and puffs are all symptoms of a phenomenon known as a "backdraft" or smoke explosion. It occurs when a fire in a confined space (or closed-up building) consumes all of the available oxygen and replaces it with smoke. As the smoke, which is no more than unburned fuel, becomes more abundant and the fire dies down, there is still enough heat to ignite combustibles but no oxygen to support it.

When a fire in a confined space is starved for oxygen, only three outcomes are possible. The first is that if the fire continues to be deprived of oxygen, it burns out. Second, firefighters vent the fire by cutting a large hole(s) in the highest part of the roof above the involved fire area. Simultaneously, other firefighters attack the fire from below with hose lines. Third, and the worst case, fresh oxygen is admitted below or at the fire level, and an explosion of expanding fire and pressure results. This is a backdraft. Most of the firefighters at the park that evening believed that is what happened.

The Quonset roof was more than fifteen feet above the ceiling in the center of the hall. Smoke travels upward during a structure fire. Once the smoke is obstructed by a ceiling or a roof it starts to bank back down. One can only imagine the quantity of smoke that spacious attic contained before atmospheric pressure and heat forced it down through access panel openings in the walls.

The small utility access openings in the walls, concealed by the ceiling between the hall and the kitchen and the hall and the cocktail lounge, allowed the smoke to travel horizontally and build up in the ceiling cavities before being forced downward and discovered. Those ceiling cavities were air spaces in the walls and the hall's attic, and small areas about one foot high above the ceilings in the lounge and kitchen. Given all the smoke available, had there been more heat in the attic the explosion would have been much greater, forcing many of the four by eight-foot cellulose ceiling panels down onto the scattering patrons.

Another part of Brophy's report addresses the fire that occurred in the hall ceiling during a bingo game about a year and a half earlier, in 1954. A fire broke out in the motor of a ceiling fan, and smoke was seen coming from the ceiling around the device. As the games continued, the fire department was called and Roy Helms climbed the trap door ladder. Just before the Brooklyn engine arrived, Roy put out the fire with a fire extinguisher. The building was never evacuated, even while the firefighters lowered the damaged fan from the ceiling.[27]

According to Brophy, Arundel Park was not without electrical problems. He interviewed Ralph Smith of the Boulevard Electric Company, which installed all of the electrical wiring in the main building at the time it was built. He also wired later additions such as the milk bar, kitchen, and cocktail lounge. He did not install the neon lights, only the power lines to their transformers. Smith claimed that the Underwriters Electrical Division ordered Arundel Park to reduce the current supplied to the lighted boards that displayed the bingo numbers inside the hall from 110 volts to 12 volts. That was never done, and the building's insurance premium was increased by 25 percent.

Brophy's report concluded: "No evidence of negligence on the part of anyone in connection with the cause of the fire had been disclosed." He also concluded that the explosion in the attic was caused by a "backdraft," and that was that. The world's most famous fire investigator basically confirmed the findings of the county and state investigating team. It is interesting but not unusual that Arundel Park's hired investigator did not address the locked exit doors.[28]

Harry Klasmeier had an opportunity to discuss his committee's findings with Arundel Park's private investigator. Although the two discussed the fire and compared notes, neither Klasmeier nor anyone else on the committee ever saw Brophy's final document.[29]

On the evening of February 28, 1956, the investigating committee completed their own thirty-page report and made a two-hour presentation to the county commissioners on the fire's cause and other conditions that led to the tragedy. In the commissioners' meeting room on the second floor of the county court house on Church Circle in Annapolis, Klasmeier presented tape recordings of eyewitness accounts, photographs, and charred bits of evidence, all gathered during the month-long investigation.[30] Their report was borne of "painstaking scrutiny" of the ruins and contained a detailed and technical study of the physical evidence. Something like a hundred witnesses (well short of the projected five hundred) had been interviewed and their statements recorded. The document included medical reports from the victims' autopsies.[31]

Harry Klasmeier explained that the inquiry had been difficult, since most of the physical evidence was destroyed in the fire. To help the board understand the impact of the extreme heat, the investigators provided charred brass fittings, and melted window panes and soft drink bottles for the members to examine. The glass had melted in temperatures believed to have been in the neighborhood of 1,860 degrees Fahrenheit.

The presentation itself grew heated when Klasmeier discussed the Fire Underwriters Rating Bureau report. The chief fire marshal had seen a copy, but he emphasized that since the underwriters bureau was a private business

The NFPA's Richard Stevens and Fire Marshal Harry Klasmeier adhered to the theory that the fire was caused by a spark or a faulty chimney flue from the exterior fireplace attached to the south wall of the kitchen. (Gary Utz.)

that established insurance rates, it did not like to elaborate on its inspections. "You will find that they [rating bureau] are not going to comment on the fire safety of the building. They are privately owned and do not like to get involved in controversies." Detective Thomas Smith added, "The committee sent a written letter requesting the report, but we still have not received a copy. . . . The rating bureau has been uncooperative."

Klasmeier continued, "I feel the report would not have much bearing on the fire causes."

"It [has] a bearing as far as the county government is concerned!" snapped Ralph Lowman, chair of the county commission.[32]

Klasmeier went on, "I inspected the auditorium last March and found

A little league baseball scoreboard and field, evidence of a more innocent time, behind the closest and only fire hydrant on the grounds of the once enchanting Arundel Park. (Lorretta Kane Dove.)

it in clean condition with more than the required number of hand fire extinguishers and a privately installed fire hydrant outside the building. A standpipe and fire hose had been later installed in the building." Klasmeier said that he thought the owner of the auditorium was indeed "fire conscious," and that the fire smoldered across the inner surface of the ceiling for several hours before bursting into flames. By then it was too big to be handled by hand-held fire extinguishers.

The investigators concluded that the fire had begun in the kitchen ceiling. It had burned for a long time before breaking through to the outside of the building, where a small fire was observed shortly before flames filled the interior. Smoldering but lacking sufficient air to develop into flame, the

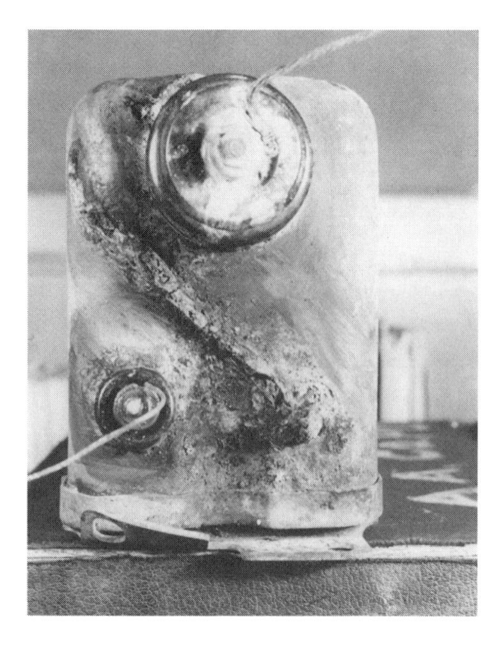

The charred neon light transformer, located in the ceiling of the kitchen, believed to have shorted out and caused the fire. (Gary Utz.)

fire slowly expanded over a "vast area of the hall ceiling." The unseen fire produced a great volume of flammable vapors, smoke, and carbon monoxide gas that later erupted and created the flash fire reported by the hall's occupants. Interviews with survivors established that a number of people smelled smoke long before the fire was discovered but thought it came from the wood fire on which cooks were roasting oysters.

Opening the trap door and admitting fresh oxygen ignited the gases and vapors above the ceiling, causing them to erupt into flame. The accelerated blaze coupled with the loss of the hall's lights caused the panic. According to Klasmeier's report, "This is when panic prevailed and people fought for exits. Many were knocked down or lost their footing and were trampled." Many who fell to the floor were picked up and carried outside. Fallen chairs and overturned tables, from which all glassware had been knocked to the floor, added to the confusion and injuries.

In calling the patrons' inability to immediately open the double door at the west end of the building a "fatal delay," investigators had to be referring to the double door between the hall and the milk bar. The report credited Frank Kvech Jr. with locating and operating the latch that opened the large overhead door at the west end of the building after many others had tried and failed. But it was also "very probable" that the time needed to open that door "caused a huge crowd to accumulate at that point resulting in a fatal delay."

In addressing the deaths, the investigating committee noted: "[The] outcome of the autopsy examination of the bodies of the victims dispelled earlier theories that they had been trampled or burned to death. The carbon monoxide content of the victims' lungs and blood ranged from a saturation of 60% to 70%, sufficient to cause death. The bodies of [9] victims found in one corner of the building could point to a higher concentration of deadly [carbon] monoxide gas in that area than in other sections of the building." The investigators advanced the possibility that the surging crowd had pressed the victims, all women, into the corner where they had succumbed to carbon monoxide before they could fight their way out.

The committee pointed out that a short circuit was discovered in the area over the kitchen where the two smaller fires had been seen, and might have ignited other materials in the ceiling. A charred neon light transformer was provided for the commissioners to see and inspect. H. Charles Robertson explained that it had been mounted over the kitchen and bore indications that a short-circuited wire had been attached to it. A short circuit (sometimes called a dead short) is usually created when connecting wires to an appliance or other electrical device are loose. The loose connection may cause a hot electric arch, which has sufficient intensity to melt the wire and possibly start a fire. Robertson believed the wire had touched off the fire, though he could not prove it.[33] Although the investigators agreed it was possible the blaze was the result of spontaneous combustion, that theory is weak given the evidence of the short circuit.

Prominent in the report was that no one notified the Brooklyn Fire Department until at least thirteen minutes after fire was first seen in the exterior wooden cornice near the roof of the kitchen. The committee attributed the delay to the fact that Arundel Park employees and others were not seriously concerned with that fire or the second small fire in the kitchen and attempted to extinguish both themselves. The investigators concluded the obvious: "An immediate call to the fire department might have averted loss of life."

Richard Stevens, from the NFPA, reported that some eight minutes elapsed between the fire's first sighting from outside the building and the start of the evacuation. "During that time different individuals attempted to

Dr. Wm. B. D. Penniman
1856-1938
Dr. Arthur Lee Browne
1867-1932

Executive Officers
George D. Penniman, Jr.
W. Moss
Dante G. Beretta
Harry M. Burkholder

Mulberry 5-5811
Cable Address - "Baltest"

PENNIMAN & BROWNE, Inc.

CHEMISTS–ENGINEERS–INSPECTORS
341 St. Paul Place
BALTIMORE 2, MARYLAND

Washington, D. C. Office
412 Albee Bldg., 15th and G Sts., N. W., (5)
Republic 7-5066

Warehouse
313 Hargrove Alley

X-Ray Laboratory and
Experimental Grounds
6252 Falls Road
Balto. 9 Valley 5-6511

ATTENTION: Mr. H. Charles Robertson
Special Investigator

February 15, 1956

ANALYTICAL DIVISION

REPORT OF ANALYSIS

No. 560386

Sample of Fiberboard

From Anne Arundel County Police Dept.

Marked As below

MARKED	"M - from Main Ceiling Arena"	"K - from Kitchen Ceiling"
Ash	2.39 %	1.19 %
Self-ignition Temperature	490°F	440°F
Microscopic and chemical identification	Cellulose	Cellulose

The low ash content of these specimens corresponds to a cellulose-type board with possibly some binder, and indicates the samples are not a mineral type board or mineral filler.

A microscopic examination of the specimens indicated that both consisted of the cellulose-type of fiber. This was confirmed by a positive chemical test for cellulose on each sample. Cane fiberboard is a typical example of such cellulose-type.

Both specimens were extremely flammable, igniting readily with the flame of a match and continuing to burn. Autogeneous ignition temperatures of 490°F and 440°F on the "M" and "K" samples, respectively, were obtained. In our ignition temperature determinations we observed variances which may have been influenced to some extent by the preheating or slight charring of the specimens. The loss of some volatile constituents due to preheating could cause, in our opinion, an appreciable change in ignition temperature of the fiberboard.

PENNIMAN & BROWNE, INC.
H. M. Burkholder
H. M. Burkholder

SM FORM 24 6-55 HMSCO.

fight the fire," he noted. "Failure to evacuate the building on detection of fire or to call the fire department was the primary cause of the loss of life." The committee's final conclusion was that the deaths resulted from the delay in opening the large overhead door at the western end of the building.

Regarding the fire codes, Klasmeier noted that the county codes were more lenient than those established by the National Fire Protection Association (NFPA), even though the National Board of Fire Underwriters had scrutinized the county codes and judged them to be "in line with good fire prevention practice." Klasmeier preferred the NFPA standards and urged they be applied to all county buildings. "The desired capacity limits of county buildings will be the subject of future discussions by public officials," he assured the commissioners.

Klasmeier, Robertson, Gleim, and Thomas S. Smith, signed the report. Chairman Ralph Lowman expressed the hope it would help prevent fires in the future.[34]

In April 1956, the Anne Arundel County Grand Jury completed its investigation, concluding that the county was "singularly" free from illegal gambling and organized crime. Their report also requested a revision of the Anne Arundel County Fire Prevention Code.[35]

WITHIN A MONTH OF THE Arundel Park fire, another incident brought about a review of the county's emergency response capabilities along with the critical care standards of area hospitals. The controversy arising from the Arundel Park fire was already having an effect.

On February 23, 1956, at approximately 5:26 A.M., Chief Wilbur Wade, Detective Gleim of the county police, Thomas Smith of the state police, and H. Charles Robertson, met at the Ferndale Police Station to discuss the Arundel Park Fire Investigation Report. Discussion came to an abrupt end when a fourteen-car Pennsylvania Railroad passenger train traveling from Washington to New York derailed at high speed and six cars smashed into a secluded and isolated area in the community of Severn. Upon hearing of the crash, Wade, Gleim, Robertson, and Smith ran out to their patrol cars in the parking lot and rushed to the scene of the accident.[36]

A laboratory report concerning the highly combustible ceiling tile that burned like a "stack of cardboard egg crates" when the fire broke through the ceiling of the main assembly hall. (Author's collection.)

This passenger train of the Pennsylvania Railroad crashed in Severn, Maryland, killing six and injuring hundreds—a grim reminder of the Arundel Park tragedy. (Courtesy of the Hearst Corporation.)

The train had been traveling at eighty miles per hour when it jumped the tracks near Florida Avenue. Two dining cars bore the brunt of the crash. One car slammed into one of the steel poles holding up the railroad's electric catenary lines—the lines that maintain contact with the powerful GG1 electric engine and provide its power. The collision split the car in half. Five people died and about a hundred were transported to area hospitals. For most of the police and rescue workers it was a grim reminder of the Arundel Park oyster roast only twenty-six days earlier for which the same swift pattern of assistance had been set up.[37]

The Baltimore Civil Defense agency conducted a review of the responses

An Anne Arundel County police officer stands with officials and rescue workers examining the wreckage the morning after the crash. Criticism in the wake of the Arundel Park fire had led to improved communications, which allowed South Baltimore General Hospital to be notified in advance and have time to prepare for the arrival of the injured. (Courtesy of the Hearst Corporation.)

to both incidents, the Arundel Park fire and the train wreck. Their investigators collected and studied information on behavior at both sites, the distribution of casualties by ambulance, and the treatment they received at area hospitals.[38] Anne Arundel County did not fare well in their evaluation of communications, emergency organization, and incident command and control. The report criticized the county's ambulance response, concluding that there was no "central control over ambulance movement." It also emphasized the uncontrolled movement of police cars, private cars, and other volunteer vehicles transporting the injured to doctors and hospitals. One of its recommendations called for area-wide emergency planning.[39]

With regard to hospitals, the Civil Defense study cited inadequate parking and discharging facilities, and the inability to control excited crowds and anguished relatives. It also examined the way medical personnel were distributed between the hospital and the accident site, the coordination between Red Cross and Civil Defense services, and the integration of medical with non-medical facilities.[40]

The final report conceded that the Arundel Park fire and the train wreck were both extreme situations. Nevertheless, communications were faulty, coordination among authorities was defective, and command over the people and vehicles at the incident sites was poor. Control over the medical phases of organization, first aid, and ambulance distribution was also unsatisfactory.[41] A health center and casualty clearing station a few blocks down Belle Grove Road should have been utilized in the Arundel Park fire, since it was equipped with stretchers, dressings, and antibiotics. Unused, too, was a county plan, created in 1954, under which the health officer, as the medical chief for the county civil defense organization, is notified and sets up the center with volunteers and physicians. On the evening of the Arundel Park fire, the health officer was never officially contacted and the plan never activated.[42] Ambulance drivers relied on their own discretion in taking patients for treatment. Most drove to the nearest hospital or the one with which they were most familiar. Hospitals were not alerted to the Arundel Park fire until the first wave of patients arrived. Information on patients was taken only at the hospital and not by the emergency providers.[43]

As a result of the Arundel Park fire, South Baltimore General Hospital immediately made improvements. It added several unlisted telephone lines to preserve the ability to make outgoing calls during emergencies. It also added a radio receiver set to the ambulance service frequency. Located in the emergency room, the radio would be staffed around the clock.[44] Henceforth the emergency room could monitor ambulance traffic and have advance warning in emergencies.

The Red Cross organized a new communications unit that would respond to disaster sites. A representative, equipped with a two-way radio would get to the scene, survey the damage, and radio his driver, who would relay the information back to the office. From Red Cross headquarters, county health officers would be notified to implement emergency plans.[45]

In the twenty-six days between the Arundel Park fire and the train wreck, the lessons learned from the fire had taken hold and been implemented. All hospitals were notified in advance. South Baltimore General monitored the ambulance radio traffic and was ready when the injured from the wreck arrived. This time its switchboard did not overload. Still, serious problems remained. Issues with ambulance response and hospital transport would not fully be resolved for another ten years, until Anne Arundel County finally created a fire department headquarters and fire alarm dispatching center in the fall of 1966.[46]

11

Finding Answers

Although the committee appointed to investigate the Arundel Park fire had only been charged with two objectives—determining its cause and learning what had led to panic and the deaths of ten victims—the urgency and general nature of their mission meant that they had no incentive to conduct a comprehensive technical and detailed investigation. The four-member team ruled out arson and attributed the start of the fire in the kitchen ceiling to an electrical short or spontaneous combustion. They evidently agreed, based on what was found during the autopsies, that the victims died from carbon monoxide poisoning. Contributing to the carbon monoxide poisoning were problems in opening the overhead door on the west side of the building, and the panicked, pressing crowd.[1]

The only bright spot in this otherwise dark tragedy, was when the National Fire Protection Association (NFPA) came to the county's assistance and conducted an independent investigation. Dedicated to preventing loss of life and property from fire, the NFPA develops and sets fire protection standards. The organization routinely sends out experts to investigate fires that involve multiple deaths or result in large property loss. From these investigations, technical as well as general recommendations are developed and proposed to improve fire safety codes and fire fighting techniques.

This was the county's first opportunity to work with a leading national

The remains of the milk bar. (Gary Utz.)

fire protection organization, and it provided the county fire marshal's office with a conduit for obtaining information on state-of-the-art fire protection practices to help prevent and control future fires. Today, Harry Klasmeier will acknowledge that in the winter of 1956 "we were still learning." The Anne Arundel County Fire Prevention Bureau had only been in existence for a year and a half. During those eighteen months, Klasmeier spent most of his time dealing with the fire safety hazards in the county public schools.

In January 1956, he closed down the Millersville Special School. Housing the county's physically disabled and mentally challenged students, it was located in a wood-framed structure in a rural area approximately twenty miles south of Brooklyn. The building had no built-in fire protection such as sprinklers and fire alarm systems. To make matters worse, there were no fire stations or fire hydrants nearby. With so many violations of the fire code, the school was an accident waiting to happen. On Klasmeier's first inspection visit, he asked the teacher substituting for the principal to activate a portable warning device that served as the building's fire alarm. The teacher replied that the device was locked in the principal's desk, that he was not present, and that she didn't have the key. Obviously the school failed the inspection. Newspapers quoted Klasmeier's statement that the building was clearly a fire trap.[2]

When he began working with the NFPA, Klasmeier learned how model codes are utilized to lessen or eliminate hazards to life during a fire. He became a member and served on committees that developed fire regulations. Through this association, he met other fire marshals and fire protection engineers across the country and exchanged experiences and information. He learned how local governments could put teeth into fire regulations by writing them into local ordinances and legislation. Although stricter fire codes for the county were still several years away, Klasmeier's involvement with the NFPA laid the groundwork for the future adoption of the much needed Life Safety Code.

Richard Stevens, an NFPA staff fire protection engineer, and Harry Klasmeier spent a great deal of time together investigating the ruins, evaluating evidence, and discussing the Arundel Park fire. Unlike the majority of the investigating committee, the two leaned toward the possibility that sparks from the fireplace or the transformer short-circuit were the most likely ignition sources. They seemed to think that sparks from a possibly

The fireplace outside the kitchen. Note the blackened wall (upper left) near where the fire started. (Loretta Kane Dove.)

defective chimney flue attached to the fireplace used to roast the oysters may have ignited the eaves of the roof earlier in the day. The fire then smoldered for hours in the wooden cornice and possibly caused the blaze.[3]

Stevens wrote a separate, independent report for the NFPA that was published in the March–April issue of the *NFPA Quarterly*, a journal available to fire chiefs, inspectors, investigators, and fire protection engineers. It reviewed case histories of devastating and deadly fires and discussed recommendations for improved fire protection practices. Stevens's report, which is far more technical and comprehensive then the county's, reviewed the facts as they coincided with the NFPA Building Exits Code. That code was by consensus the model for addressing life safety from fire in buildings of all types and uses.[4] Jurisdictions now routinely adopt these regulations through city, county, or township ordinances, or state legislation, but, even with all of the controversy that followed from the Arundel Park fire, the NFPA Building Exits Code, also known as Life Safety Code 101, would not be adopted into Maryland regulations until after 1964, eight years after the fatal fire.[5]

Stevens addressed what he believed to be six major factors that contributed to the fire's origin, the spread of fire and smoke, panic, deaths, and injuries. Unlike the county and Brophy reports, it provides a more scientific approach to addressing the developments that led to the victims' deaths. The six major factors identified in Stevens's NFPA report constitute the basis for a comprehensive analysis of this fire.

Delay in evacuation and alarm transmission. Failure to evacuate the building and contact the fire department as soon as the fire was detected was the primary cause of the loss of life. At least eight minutes passed between the time the fire was detected in the attic over the kitchen and the time the fire department was alerted. (The county report placed the time at thirteen minutes.) Facility employees, trained and empowered by management to contact the fire department and evacuate the building immediately upon the detection of the fire, would have made a major difference.[6]

One of the employees had to walk some distance to notify Roy Helms, who was working in the front office. It should be noted that in 1956 the office phone was a rotary dialing device and one of only two phones in the building (The other was in the cocktail lounge).[7] As soon as fire was detected in the wooden cornice near the roof outside the building, the fire department should have been contacted and a swift and orderly evacuation of the building begun.

Combustible concealed attic. Combustibles in the attic, such as the wooden roof, the wooden components of the arched truss assembly, and the upper side of the combustible fiberboard ceiling material—a little less than half an inch thick, created an ideal playground for an undetected fire.

Of all these combustible components, the fiberboard or celotex was the real culprit. Fiberboard was popular with builders for ceiling construction from the 1930s through the early 1960s. It was light for ease and speed of installation, and it was cheap. Although the "Celotex" company was one of many that manufactured the product, the panels were generally known by that name. This material may still be found today in club basement ceilings in older houses, in larger metropolitan areas, and in older businesses as a sub-ceiling between the roof joists and newer dropped ceiling panels. Also called fibercane, the material has a cornhusk or a sugarcane residue base and is highly combustible. According to Frank Brannigan, an expert on fire and the dangers of building materials, "Years ago [the fiberboard] industry vigorously fought attempts at regulating fiberboard. In one case, regulations were characterized as taking the bread out of the mouths of Louisiana cane farmers."[8]

At Arundel Park, the fiberboard was nailed to the underside of the roof truss. The attic or top side of the board was covered with rock wool batting insulation, four inches thick.[9] Harry Klasmeier believes that for a long time the fire smoldered in small pockets of air between the topside of the fibercane ceiling beneath the paperbacked rock wool insulation laid over the ceiling in the attic.[10] The fiberboard smoldered until it was paper thin, and as the fire broke through the ceiling in several places, it contributed heavily to the panic. Once the fire broke out, it pre-heated the hall side of the fiberboard ceiling tile causing it to ignite more quickly and spread more rapidly, gaining intensity in a "snowball effect."

What is truly sad about this is that the fire hazards of fiberboard were widely known to fire prevention and fire engineering professionals well before the Arundel Park fire. From the early 1940s fiberboard ceiling tile had been known as a dangerous interior finish that contributed to many deaths, injuries, and property loss. In 1943 a fire ripped through the Beverly Recreation Hall and Cocktail Lounge in Chicago. The building, which also housed a bowling alley, had a combustible fiberboard ceiling, which contributed heavily to the fire's spread. Although reports are sketchy, it is known that a number of people were killed and about a hundred more were injured. Many of the victims were said to have burned to death.[11] Another tragic fire occurred in 1949 at the Saint Anthony's hospital in Effingham, Illinois. The fire's spread was enhanced mainly by the fiberboard ceiling tile and resulted in seventy-four deaths, many of whom were infants in a nursery and the nurses and nuns who refused to leave them. After investigating the fire the NFPA reported the hazards of the combustible tile. Enraged manufacturers of fiberboard threatened the NFPA with legal action.[12]

Only a year before the Arundel Park fire, three children died in a house in South Amboy, New Jersey, when a fire that started from an oil stove in the first floor living room ignited the fiberboard walls and ceiling. It spread quickly across the ceiling and into the kitchen, where an open stairway led to the children's sleeping rooms on the second floor.[13] A little over a month later, a food market in Meridian, Mississippi, caught fire. "The fiberboard ceiling tile contributed to the fast fire spread that swept through the 7,500 square foot building causing over $104,000.00 in damage." Fortunately no one was injured.[14]

World War II had a significant impact on the use of fiberboard for construction. Temporary housing, funded through the federal government, was constructed in metropolitan areas to accommodate the millions of workers and their families migrating to the cities to work in defense related industries. Many buildings resembled army barracks—wood-frame structures attached to a poured concrete truss and post assembly to keep them off of the ground. They could be rapidly assembled and quickly inhabited by the workers' families. Interior walls and ceilings were covered with combustible fiberboard.[15]

The real hazards of fiberboard surfaced in 1954, less then two years before the Arundel Park fire, in Cheektowaga, New York. A small suburb of Buffalo, Cheektowaga was home to the Cleveland Hill Elementary School. During the war, numerous temporary barrack-style buildings had been added to area schools to accommodate the children of war workers. Almost ten years after the end of the war, those buildings still remained.

In an NFPA investigative report, Richard E. Stevens, the same man who later investigated the Arundel Park fire, found that the school had decided to use a classroom in one of the temporary buildings as the music room. One April morning in 1954, while thirty sixth-grade students were trying on caps and gowns for the upcoming May graduation, a fire broke out in a teacher's workroom. It spread quickly through the workroom's paneled wooden door and shot across the building's fiberboard-covered ceiling corridor. In seconds the fire forced its way into the music room, trapping the mostly ten-, eleven-, and twelve-year-olds. Two teachers and the cap and gown salesmen broke out the glass panels in the huge double wooden window sashes and pushed the kids out of the jagged glass openings. Not all escaped. Ten children died in the fire. Five more, who had escaped, later died in the hospital from burns. The death toll comprised nine girls and six boys. Nineteen others were burned.[16]

Unfortunately for the residents of Brooklyn, Maryland, and even more so the people in Chicago who would be confronted by deadly fire in 1958 at the Our Lady of Angels School, the Cleveland Hill school disaster had little national significance. It is almost inconceivable that the dangers of fiberboard were not addressed by the nation's fire protection community.

Another problem with fiberboard ceiling tile was that when burning it tended to fall from its mountings in large flaming pieces. Numerous cases of this hazard are on record. Falling fiberboard is probably the reason one of the survivors at Arundel Park claimed the fire burned the shoes off her feet.[17] As pieces of the burning fiberboard were falling and blowing through the hall, the woman without realizing it probably stepped on a burning or smoldering panel that then became stuck on the heel of her shoe.

Although testing apparatus had been invented and by 1948 was being used by the Underwriters' Laboratories, the test result data were only used to create tentative standards on flame spread. No stringent regulations on interior finish would appear until the mid-1960s. Even if Arundel Park had been built in 1956, installation of the combustible fiberboard ceiling tile would have been legal.[18]

Early editions of the Building Exits Code did not contain any regulations on interior finish. Untreated fiberboard ceiling was partly responsible for rapid fire spread in buildings, according to an article Robert S. Mouton wrote for the *NFPA Quarterly* in July 1961.[19] Not until 1969 would the Fire

Scores Trampled Fleeing Blaze at Oyster Roast Attended by Over 1000

(Other Pictures on Page 15.)

At least 12 persons were killed and hundreds were injured last night when fire and resulting panic swept a church supper in Brooklyn Park, on the south edge of Baltimore in Anne Arundel County.

Police estimated that 1000 persons were present at an oyster roast and dance sponsored by the St. Rose of Lima Catholic Church at Arundel Park Hall, a quonset-type structure.

Firemen said the holocaust began when a small blaze broke out in a duct near the wooden ceiling over the kitchen. Several men climbed ladders to attempt to put it out.

"Suddenly," one eyewitness reported, "the fire shot out all along the ceiling—almost like an explosion." The crowd, which had been orderly and had been offering wisecracking advice to the firefighters, suddenly panicked.

Leo A. Rust, an oil refinery worker who attended the oyster roast with his wife and two daughters, said the fire spread "as if somebody had spread gasoline over the place."

Undated newspaper clipping. (Patrick Prendergast.)

Prevention Bureau require Anne Arundel County Public Schools to have the fiberboard ceilings throughout the school system painted with a special fire retardant paint. Unfortunately fiberboard continued to appear in new buildings, and more would die before builders stopped using the combustible material in new construction in the mid-1960s.

Today all interior finishes including ceiling material must meet strict flame spread requirements as established in the NFPA Life Safety Code.[20] Present day ceiling tile, for the most part is non-combustible and will not burn. In addition, today's codes would have required the hall and the large concealed area in the attic of Arundel Park to be protected by automatic sprinkler systems and draft stops. Draft stops are layers of non-combustible sheetrock installed tight to the top of the ceiling and tight to the underside of the roof. They act as giant fire stops. Draft stops are required to subdivide the area into smaller fire zones to either confine the fire or significantly slow its horizontal movement.[21]

Panic. Fire, smoke, failure of the lighting system, and congestion caused by the loose folding chairs and tables were the significant factors contributing to the panic. In addition, alcohol consumption probably caused the erratic behavior observed in a number of patrons during the attempt to escape the burning structure, worsening the panic.[22]

Interestingly, the panic was not universal. On the east side of the building, where the large overhead door had been opened, there appears to have been little panic. The fire started on this side, yet according to Frank Kvech III, everyone seemed to move through the door without much difficulty. Frank heard no screaming as he and his friend left through the opened door.[23] Everywhere else panic broke out and escalated.

The five-mile-per-hour wind that evening was also from the southeast, which in all likelihood transformed the large overhead door opening into a huge fan blowing toxic smoke, fire, and heat away from the east overhead doorway to the southwest and northwest areas of the hall.[24] The air blowing inside through that doorway actually protected the occupants on the east side by pushing the fire and smoke away from them. That created havoc in the rest of the building and supplied fresh oxygen to the fire, accelerating its consumption of the combustible fiberboard ceiling.

A fire also pulls air into its base as hot air currents rise. This process

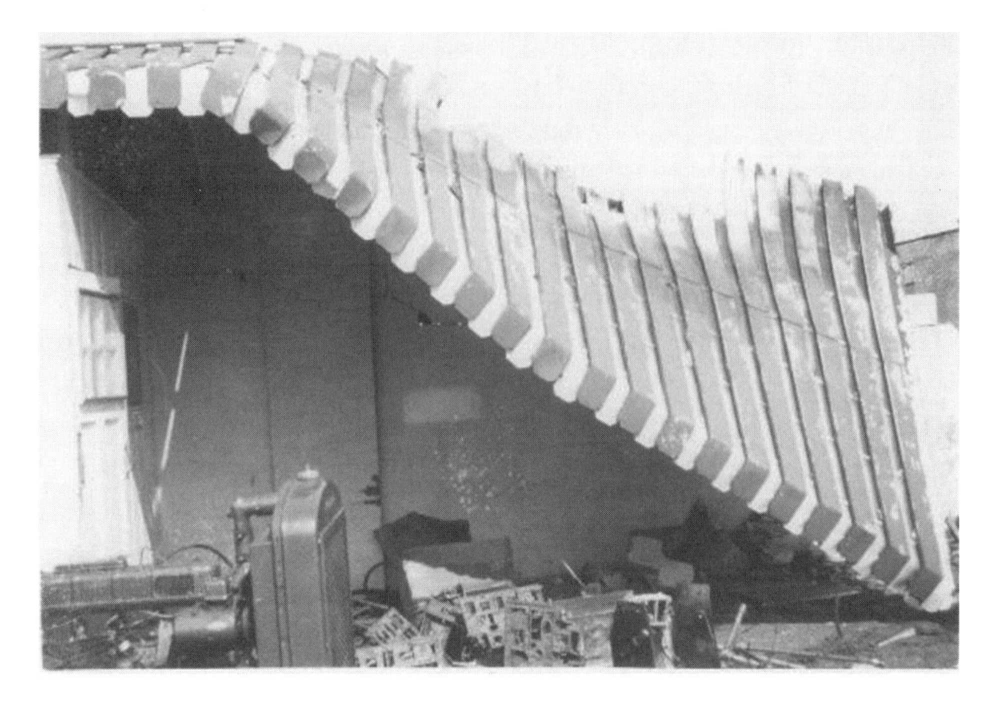

Arundel Park's emergency gasoline-powered generator (lower left), at the rear (south) of the building, never activated when the assembly hall's lights suddenly went out. (Lorretta Kane Dove.)

undoubtedly increased the speed at which fresh oxygen entered the building through the opened east side overhead doorway, so its opening contributed significantly to the fire's spread. Had the large overhead door on the east side not been opened, perhaps more people might have escaped without smoke and fire breathing down their backs.

Interesting, too, is that Stevens did not mention the locked exits as a contributor to the panic (they were only noted as being locked on a drawing of the building plan). According to the reports, most of the initially threatened occupants moved first to the northeast door opening—the oyster roast/cloakroom entrance—but on finding it blocked by those who were trying to retrieve coats, flowed toward the milk bar exit approximately forty feet away. But the milk bar double door exit, the largest in the building, was locked, and no one has been able to learn how much time passed before it was opened. The delay must have contributed greatly to the panic, as many people then rushed to the large overhead door at the west wall.

Fire life safety studies have shown that most people in an assembly, whether in an emergency or not, leave by the same way they entered. Today's Life Safety Code addresses this practice by requiring exit doors in the main wall of an entrance to be able to safely accommodate 50 percent of the occupants.[25] What is especially puzzling is that Arundel Park's north exits originally met that requirement. Yet, at some point after the structure was built and before the fire, the six-foot-wide exit doorway leading from the hall through the cloakroom corridor to the double exit doors was reduced to three feet, negating the benefit. The 50 percent front entrance exit door standard was a requirement under the old building code. Whether the door was modified before or after Klasmeier's inspection in March 1955 is unknown, but that alteration, along with the locked double doors into the milk bar, severely impeded patrons' ability to escape and heightened the panic.[26]

Overhead doors are not considered exits and are not counted as exits when determining the number of exit doorways needed. They are not considered exits because of the problems revealed during this tragedy—the pushing, which bent the door, and the problems unlatching, raising, and keeping the door open. Because the fire moved so rapidly and created so much toxic smoke, we will never know whether opened overhead doors would have allowed more occupants to escape.

Failure of the [electrical] current supply to the exit signs. The failure of the lighting system, and concurrently the lights for the exit signs, undoubtedly contributed to the panic. Although the building had a gasoline-powered generator in a room adjacent to the rear of the structure, it was not used.[27] Investigators have not learned whether this generator was dedicated to emergencies or intended for other purposes. If it was for emergencies, it is unknown whether it had to be manually started or came on automatically.

At the time of the fire, the NFPA Building Exits Code required emergency lighting (exit lights) to be wired into an independent source isolated from the general lighting so the current to the illuminated exit signs would not be interrupted in the event the normal lighting service was lost, and if so, it would be backed up by an alternative power source. Unknown too, but doubtful, is whether the illumination cast by the exit lights alone would have reduced the panic that erupted when the main lights went out. NFPA technical secretary Robert Moulton writes, "Unexpected darkness is disturbing anytime, and in time of danger, real or imagined, it is conducive

The "No Parking" sign painted on the front wall of the milk bar seems oddly out of place. (Lorretta Kane Dove.)

to panic." He continued: "Failure of lighting has been a major contributing factor in many notorious fires in the past 50 years, Iroquois Theater, Coconut Grove, and the recent Oyster Roast Fire. In these and many other fires, loss of life might have occurred even if illumination had been maintained, but the conclusion is inescapable that panic and resultant loss of life was greatly aggravated by the darkness."[28]

Today the Life Safety Code requires exit lights to be wired on a separate circuit independent of the general lighting system or be provided with a battery backup.[29] More importantly, emergency lighting, usually battery-powered, is installed and wired so that if the normal lighting is lost, these lights will illuminate and assist occupants in finding the exit.

Congestion of materials in the hall. Harry Klasmeier believes that the folding chairs and tables were a major contributor to the panic and interfered with the swift escape from the building. Fixed seating, which cannot be moved, typically has adequate aisle space and exit access built into the floor arrangement. Folding chairs and tables do not. After being knocked over and thrown about in the confusion, they created a major impediment to the evacuation of the building. Klasmeier still cannot believe that this alone did not result in greater injury and loss of life at Arundel Park.[30]

Years after the fire, as he does today, the county fire marshal required the management of eating and drinking establishments in the county to provide his office with diagrams of all seating arrangements for public assembly facilities that utilized temporary furniture, including folding chairs and tables. These diagrams were reviewed to make certain that the indicated aisle spaces complied with the minimum requirements required by the NFPA Building Exits Code (now the Life Safety Code) standard. Despite the number of exits a building has, if people cannot get to them in a swift and orderly manner during an emergency, the evacuation will result in confusion and possible panic.

Lack of fire alarm system and employee training for fire emergencies. Today most buildings the size of Arundel Park are equipped with sprinklers and fire alarm systems. Even Arundel Park's successor, the newer Arundel Arena now the Bingo World, was eventually equipped with an automatic sprinkler system in 1986. But even with these systems, employees have duties in an emergency. At the time of the Arundel Park fire (and today), the NFPA Building Exits/Life Safety Code emphasized training employees for the duties they should perform in the event of fire.[31] There was no evidence that Arundel Park employees had received such instruction.

Obviously someone should have called the fire department immediately on the evening of the Arundel Park fire, and the hall's occupants should have been warned when the fire was discovered in the kitchen ceiling. Someone in authority should have cut off the band and announced over the public address system that everyone was to leave the building, to walk, not run, to the nearest exit and not stop at the cloakroom, etc. The duty to inform audiences of exits before the start of an assembly actually was required (and still is) by the county fire prevention code then in existence, but it was loosely enforced when enforced at all.[32] No one knows if such an announcement was ever made at the beginning of the oyster roast. In similar gatherings it is rarely if ever carried out today. In 1977, more than two decades after Arundel Park, the inability of an establishment's employees to make the proper notifications and evacuations figured prominently in the loss of 165 lives at the Beverly Hills Supper Club fire in Southgate, Kentucky. When the announcement to evacuate was finally made in the huge Cabaret Room, the message was delivered by a young employee whom the crowd did not take seriously.[33]

Today the NFPA Life Safety Code requires that public assembly employees be trained to perform a "laundry list" of specific actions or duties when a fire is detected.[34] This is known as an emergency plan. Employees are required to drill in these procedures and duties. In addition, the Occupational Safety and Health Administration (OSHA) regulations require an employer to develop and implement emergency plans.[35]

Employees must be trained in incipient fire suppression. Carbon dioxide (CO_2) fire extinguishers are not rated for Class A fires. The fire in Arundel Park's kitchen and hall ceilings, which consisted of ordinary combustible building materials, was a Class A fire. The CO_2 extinguishers used in the futile attempts to suppress it work well on small flammable liquid, gas, and electrical fires, but when used on Class A fires they only remove the oxygen from the flames for a few moments. They cannot penetrate a deep-seated Class A fire. Even the portable Class A soda and acid extinguishers probably would have failed because of the hot, smoldering fire's large area.

Although not required by any codes, Arundel Park did have a standpipe with fire suppression hose and a nozzle. Possibly at the request of its insurance carrier, it was installed after Klasmeier's inspection of March 1955. The system was mounted near the wall in the area of the bandstand.[36] The 150 feet of cotton standpipe hose with attached nozzle would have reached the original fire area. One or two trained employees, immediately applying a stream of water supplied by a six-inch main with the maximum pressure into the opened trap door might have created enough steam in the concealed space to greatly slow if not extinguish the fire altogether. But the day after the fire, the forged "steel" control wheel that turns on the pipe valve supplying the hose was missing, so it appears the appliance would not have worked had somebody attempted to use it.[37]

Employees should be authorized to pull the fire alarm, evacuate patrons in an orderly manner, and call the fire department. If properly trained, they can try to extinguish the fire. These things were never done at Arundel Park. If they had been, the night might have turned out much differently.

One overriding question is: Why couldn't the women get out? Why were they found so close to the exit, huddled together along the west wall of the building between the overhead door and the single exit leading out the front (or north) wall of the hall? One possible clue is based on statements made by Mr. and Mrs. James T. Dulaney. The Dulaneys were seated at a table with Mrs. Dulaney's sister Stella Kozlowski, Frances Obzut, and Mrs. Obzut's daughter, Frances Cook.[38] It is unclear where the table was located within the hall. Apparently the entire group started to leave when they first saw the smoke near the ceiling trap door on the east side. Which door they chose remains unknown.

When the flames broke out and pandemonium began, the Dulaneys looked back and saw eighty-two-year-old Frances Obzut "being swept up by the crowd." Her daughter, Frances Cook, and Stella Kozlowski went back to help her.[39] Frances Obzut's physical condition is unknown, but we can assume that at eighty-two she could not compete with the frantic and abusive crowd.[40] Did she faint or lose consciousness? Was she knocked down? Obviously, Cooke and Kozlowski were impeded in their attempt to assist her, though they were heroic to try.

Yet this possible scenario does not coincide with information provided by Joseph and Peg Ross (Rozmarynowski) in one puzzling particular. According to the Rosses, the talk in the Brooklyn community after the fire was that people had seen Stella Kozlowski *outside* the building.[41] Perhaps she had become separated from Obzut and Cooke but had found her way out and then gone back inside to search for them.

Ester Daughtery seems to have followed a similar pattern. Ester's husband, Jack, pushed her out a door and later escaped himself from a window.[42] Did Ester go back for her purse? Did she know Obzut and Cooke? Once safely outside, did she team up with Stella Kozlowski to reenter the building and try to rescue Mrs. Obzut? If these theories are even close to being accurate they could speak for four of the victims. But what about the other six?

It is a fact that Theresa Kelly, the youngest victim, almost made it out. Her husband, Liston, at one point held her at a window in a position to get

Looking east from Belle Grove Road. The large opening in the west wall is where the malfunctioning overhead door was located, where Frank Kvech Jr. saved perhaps hundreds. (Courtesy of Gary Utz.)

out, lost his grip, and was pushed away.[43] Did Theresa fall and hit her head? Was she unconscious? Was the window from which the vigorous and pretty first-grade teacher almost escaped near the place where they eventually found her and all of the other bodies?

Regarding the remaining victims, Anna Brandt, Stella Cavanugh, Gladys McKay, Josephine Franczkowski and Goldie Otto, not enough information is available to develop any theories. One victim was found near the bandstand closer to the original scene of the ceiling fire. Perhaps she was in the bathroom when all the commotion started and became lost in the dark, the smoke, and the maze of overturned tables and chairs. Maybe she was pushed, like Louise Sokolis, or fell and hit her head and lost consciousness, rendering her unable to escape the carbon monoxide fumes.

One assumption that can safely be made is that most of the victims knew one another. Cooke, Obzut, Kelly, Cavanaugh and McKay all lived within a mile and a half of one another. Franzkowski and Brandt, from East Baltimore near Eastern Avenue, lived about a quarter of a mile apart. Otto

Arundel Park, once northern Anne Arundel County's largest covered floor area, now a burned out shell. This photograph looks east from inside the west wall. (Courtesy of Lorretta Kane Dove.)

was from Rockdale and Daughtery from Manhattan Beach near Severna Park.[44] Although Stella Kozlowski lived in the city near the Alameda Shopping Center in Kenilworth Park, she along with her sister Elizabeth (Dulaney) grew up in Wagner's Point and knew many people in the Brooklyn area.[45] The deceased women were all deeply religious and had a strong faith. When found most were still clutching rosaries and religious medals.[46]

Possibly they were all trying to protect each other, hoping they could wait it out until the firefighters arrived. No one will ever know. Driven by increased air flowing from the opened overhead door on the east side, carbon monoxide gas had probably reached a very high level in the northwest corner of the hall and undoubtedly affected the women's judgment. Based on the autopsy reports, it was what killed them in the end.[47]

There is some inconsistency in accounts of the operation of the west side overhead door. According to one story it was jammed in the closed position as frightened evacuees pressed against it. At this point Frank Kvech Jr., who no doubt had experience with overhead doors driving buses and working in the garages of the Baltimore Transit System, managed to release the locking assembly and push the door up.[48] The question is, how long did it stay up? According to statements made by John Miles Jr., "The [west side] overhead door was only opened part way then lowered since it would not open completely."[49] One thing that we know for certain from Frank Kvech III is that the east overhead door stayed open. If the west overhead door had somehow been propped open, the women who were so very close to it might well have made their escape.

The application of Anne Arundel County's building code to the planning, design, and construction of Arundel Park teetered along a fine line between a lawful building and a fire trap. Arundel Park's concrete block walls with combustible wooden truss roof assemblies and a plywood roof covered with felt paper and tar was classified as "ordinary construction." The code, enacted on March 14, 1939, approximately ten years before Arundel Park was built, lays out strict requirements for "ordinary construction." In the case of "ordinary construction" in a building the size of Arundel Park (in square feet), the code imposed limitations.

A building of ordinary construction with street access on three sides was limited to 7,500 square feet. It could be exceeded and expanded up to the doubling of its size (15,000 square feet) if it was equipped with a full automatic sprinkler system. Since Arundel Park's original structure (the 160' x 80' hall) was 12,800 square feet, it was required to have the sprinkler system. With the later add-ons such as the cocktail lounge, kitchen, offices, storage, coatroom, and milk bar, the total size would come to 20,073 square feet.

Unfortunately the building code contained an exception clause that allowed a building the size of Arundel Park to be built without a sprinkler system. The exception or loophole would be found in the section entitled "Fire Limits." Fire limits were established in urban areas to limit the use of combustible materials in construction in order to reduce the possibility of a general conflagration. Wood frame construction and unprotected metal buildings were prohibited. It is unknown whether fire limits were established in the county, but along Belle Grove Road in the late 1940s, it was very doubtful. A building of "ordinary construction" exceeding area restrictions might be approved if it was constructed outside the fire limits; if it was approved by the president of the Anne Arundel County board of commissioners, the building official, and the local fire chief; and if it was

The south side of the structure looking west. (Lorretta Kane Dove.)

protected by an automatic sprinkler system for buildings of "combustible occupancy." Hence the loophole.

No official records remain to indicate whether the principals agreed or disagreed on applying the exception to Arundel Park. Nothing on record interprets the designation or defines the term "combustible occupancy." No evidence reveals why the county leadership failed to require Arundel Park to install a sprinkler system. All that is left are eleven dead, scores of injured, and pounds of debris that were cleaned up and hauled to the dump—grim numbers that could have been reversed by enforcing the sprinkler system requirement and not resorting to the loophole.[50] (See Appendix A).

12

Black Cloud

The property damage to the Arundel Park building and its contents was estimated to be $150,000.[1] According to Loretta Kane Dove, his granddaughter, Roy Helms was saddened and bothered by the events of that frightful night for the rest of his life. Soon after the fire, he received letters and telegrams from congressmen, county commissioners, and loyal bingo customers, all expressing sorrow for the loss of life and property and urging him to rebuild.[2] More than a year would pass before construction began on a new building about two hundred feet southeast of the original site.

As debris from Arundel Park was being cleaned up and hauled away and the several hearings, investigations, and reports finalized, the time came to address legal matters. Within three months of the fire, attorneys representing those who had died or been injured began filing damage suits in Baltimore City Superior Court.[3] Most suits filed on behalf of surviving family members of the deceased sought amounts ranging from $150,000 to more than $400,000 to compensate for their pain, suffering, and mental anguish. Within a year, about thirty civil suits had been filed against the Arundel Park Corporation, Father Ripple and the Saint Rose of Lima Church, and the Baltimore Catholic Archdiocese.[4] Surprisingly, they did not number in the hundreds.

A second disaster strikes sixteen years later and only a few yards from the site of Arundel Park.

The property damage to the building and its contents was estimated to be $150,000. It would be over a year before construction began for a new building about two hundred feet southeast of the original site. (Lorretta Kane Dove.)

Some of the suits claimed that the park's hall was improperly constructed and maintained. The building lacked exits, and the exits it had were inadequate and not immediately accessible. There were too few ushers and guards to control or extinguish the blaze promptly or direct patrons to safety. Other suits alleged improper inspection and argued that with "ordinary care" the fire could have been extinguished without fatalities.[5] Anne Arundel County was never named as a defendant.

To the best of the author's knowledge none of the civil actions ever went to trial, and it would be many years before they were all settled. Eventually the suits filed against, Father Ripple, Saint Rose of Lima, and the archdiocese were dropped and all complaints addressed by the park's insurance carrier. Understandably, more than ten years passed before Saint Rose of Lima sponsored another oyster roast.

As the lawsuits wound through the long legal process, generating volumes of depositions, interviews, and attorneys' motions, the black cloud

WESTERN UNION
TELEGRAM
W. P. MARSHALL, PRESIDENT

CLASS OF SERVICE
This is a fast message unless its deferred character is indicated by the proper symbol.

SYMBOLS
DL=Day Letter
NL=Night Letter
LT=International Letter Telegram

The filing time shown in the date line on domestic telegrams is STANDARD TIME at point of origin. Time of receipt is STANDARD TIME at point of destination

WM08 (31).

1956 JAN 30 PM 3 50

W BXA098 GOVT PD=BX WASHINGTON DC 30 NFT=
LEROY HELM=
BELLEGROVE RD BALTO=

PLEASE BE ASSURED THAT MY OFFICE AND I STAND READY TO RENDER ANY ASSISTANCE WHICH MAY BE NEEDED AS A RESULT OF YESTERDAYS TRAGIC FIRE AT ARUNDEL PARK=
RICHARD E LANKFORD MEMBER OF CONGRESS=

THE COMPANY WILL APPRECIATE SUGGESTIONS FROM ITS PATRONS CONCERNING ITS SERVICE

After the fire Leroy Helms received numerous letters and telegrams from elected officials and loyal bingo customers expressing sorrow for the loss of life and property. (Lorretta Kane Dove.)

that had arrived over Brooklyn on the cold, drizzly, evening of January 29, 1956, reappeared time and again. Its unlucky shadow loomed over that little mile-and-a-half stretch of Brooklyn–Brooklyn Park between Belle Grove Road and the Saint Rose of Lima Church on 4th Street for the next eleven years.

Just over four months from the night of the Arundel Park fire, August Siefert, the Brooklyn Volunteer Fire Department's one-time fire chief, was killed less then a thousand feet from where he had worked as a special policeman with Andrew Brady on the night of the fatal oyster roast. He had displayed remarkable courage that night, staying inside and helping people get out of the building until his uniform burned.[6]

In June 1956, he was again working as a special policeman. Construction of the modern highway serving Baltimore's new harbor tunnel was in full swing. Large yellow "Caterpillar" earth-moving "Pans" and dump trucks crossed Belle Grove Road back and forth countless times each day just south of 6th Avenue, filling in the massive swamp and lowlands with Brooklyn

With the building leveled and cleaned up, the Brooklyn Volunteer Fire Department continued to train on the Arundel Park parking lot in the summer of 1956. Note the construction of the I-895 bridge in the background. (Charlie Doegen and Les Helfrich.)

Park dirt to build the road that eventually would become the Harbor Tunnel Throughway, Interstate 895.

The forty-eight-year-old Siefert was directing traffic where the tractors crossed the dual-lane Belle Grove Road. From where he stood and worked day after day, he could see the fire hydrant at the corner of 6th Avenue and Belle Grove Road that had been used the night of the great fire. He could watch the Matlack truck and tanker vehicles going in and out of the facility on the east side of the road. To the south, Siefert could see the remains of the eight-inch block foundation of the once bustling Arundel Park.[7]

On Friday June 1, an accident occurred between a dump truck and a Caterpillar earthmoving tractor. Somehow, August Siefert was struck by the dump truck, knocked down, and instantly killed. The truck rolled over into a ditch on the west side of Belle Grove Road. Its driver and the Caterpillar's operator were both charged with manslaughter and reckless driving. A family man, Siefert left a wife, two sons, and a daughter behind. All were members of the Saint Rose of Lima Church. August's father, John Seifert, was one of the seven "founders" of the Saint Rose of Lima organization.[8]

Eleven years passed before the black cloud struck again. This time there was no fire, and miraculously, no loss of life.

On February 9, 1967, Father Francis O'Brien was saying mass at the children's early morning Lenten service at the Saint Rose of Lima Church. He was standing on the altar before about a hundred parishioners, mostly youngsters, when with no warning except a sound "like someone slamming a door" the entire roof of the church collapsed and buried his congregation.[9]

Brooklyn Engine 35 and Truck 21, housed in a new, concrete and brick station at Maude Avenue and 5th Street, arrived first. The entire wooden truss assembly had collapsed under the weight of the previous day's heavy snow. The only parts of the structure still recognizable were the standing brick walls. The roof, now a pile of wooden rubble, pancaked straight down on top of the wooden pews as the children and a few adults in attendance dove to the floor at the last second. Eyewitnesses said the collapse sounded like an "explosion" and described the children "as swarming like ants" out of the huge pile of rubble that moments before had been a beautiful church.[10]

A second alarm was called, with additional ambulances. Firefighters, policemen, and neighbors crawled through the debris and under the pews to rescue those who were trapped. It is almost incredible that no one was killed. Thirteen of the estimated forty-eight injured were taken to the hospital by fire department ambulances. The remaining victims with less serious wounds were treated at a field hospital set up by fire department medical officers at the scene.[11] The field hospital concept was a lesson taken from the Arundel Park tragedy.

Bill Brady's nine-year-old daughter Nadine, a student at Saint Rose of Lima, was one of the lucky. Although she received only minor cuts and bruises and had survived the most terrifying event of her life, Nadine was in tears because her mother had told her to take very good care of her new shoes, and now they were lost somewhere in the rubble.

George Feeley's seven-year-old son George and his twelve-year-old

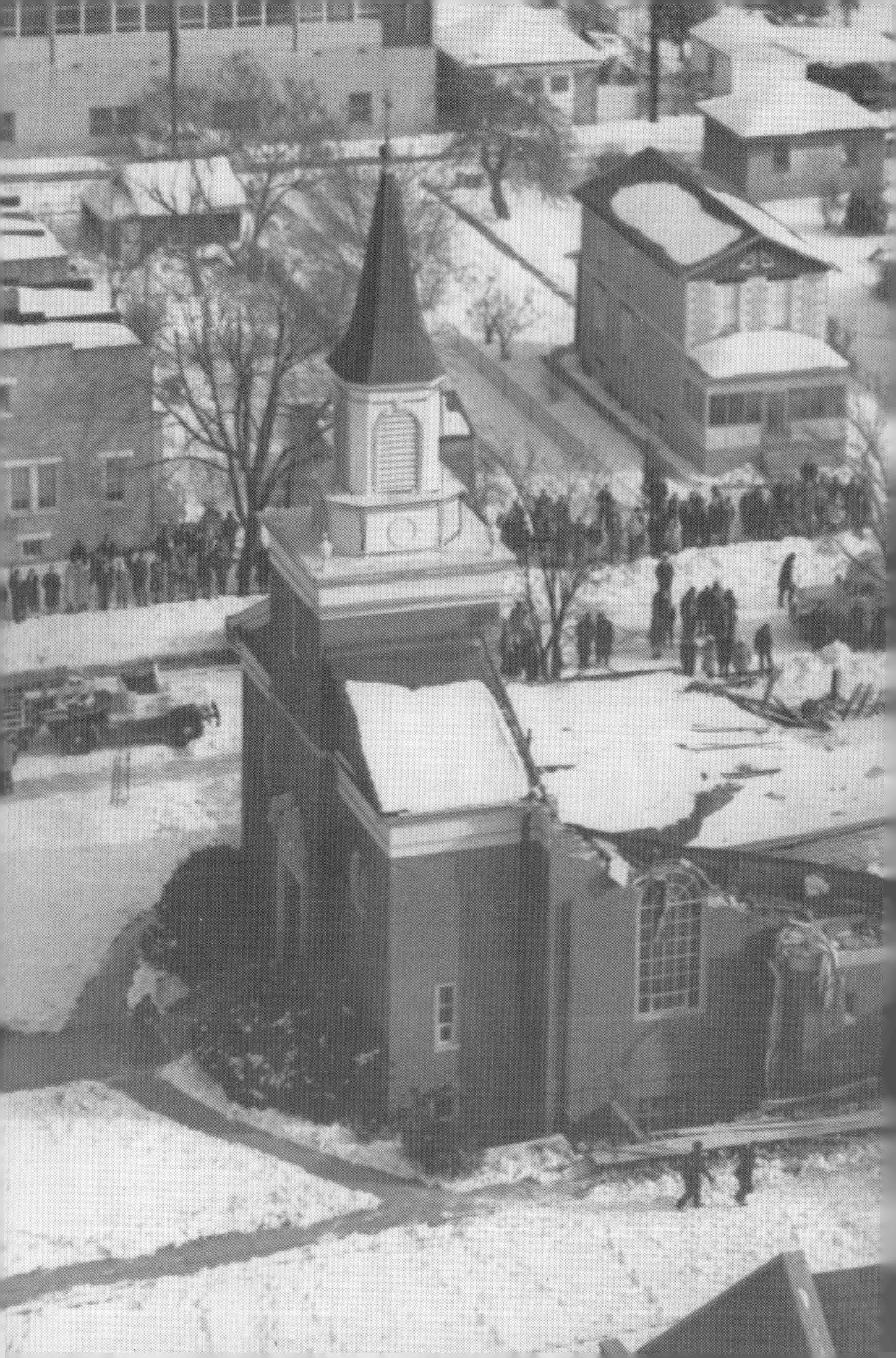

Aerial photo taken after the roof of Saint Rose of Lima Church collapsed, looking at the south side of the building. February 9, 1967. (Courtesy of Hearst Corporation.)

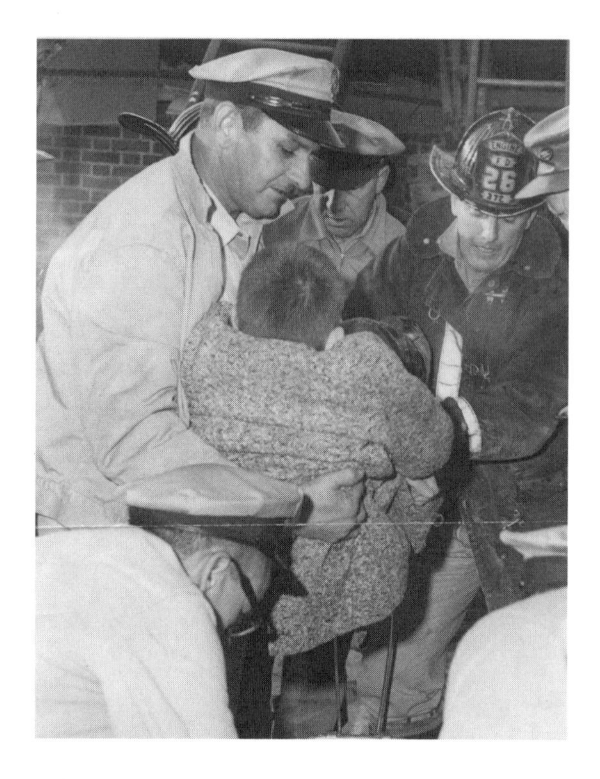

Left: Baltimore City Fire Department ambulance attendants and a firefighter place an injured Saint Rose student on an ambulance stretcher. Opposite: Firefighters and civilians search for children and teachers in the rubble. Below: Brooklyn citizens read about the tragedy from an early edition of the Baltimore News-American. (All photos courtesy of the Hearst Corporation.)

daughter Michelle also escaped the collapse with a few scrapes and cuts as the Bradys and their extended family, the Feeleys, experienced another brush with tragedy.[12]

An investigation ordered by Baltimore mayor Theodore R. McKeldin found that the incident resulted from a substandard roof assembly and shoddy construction. Low grade, unseasoned lumber, the absence of necessary joining devices, split rings, and poor load distribution caused the collapse.[13]

In the year preceding the Arundel Park fire and August Siefert's death, a set of parallel, two-lane, steel bridge spans were constructed to carry the new approach to the harbor tunnel over Belle Grove Road before it passed under the Patapsco River. The bridge, only a stone's throw south of where the Arundel Park once stood, opened for traffic in the fall of 1957. It was there, only a hundred feet from where the overhead door had been located in the west wall of Arundel Park, that the county's fire engines once more responded to the park's huge parking lot.

Fierce heat and flames confront Anne Arundel County firefighters after the collision of a tanker truck and a passenger car beneath the I-895 overpass on October 3, 1972. (Keith Hammack.)

Early on the morning of October 3, 1972, a tractor-trailer tanker truck loaded with 7,800 gallons of gasoline was traveling south on Belle Grove Road. As its twenty-five-year-old driver, Robert Fleegle, of Pennsylvania, started downhill into the Belle Grove Road turn south of 6th Avenue in the predawn darkness, he noticed a Volkswagen Beetle ahead of him.[14] As both vehicles traveled toward the Harbor Tunnel Throughway overpass, the driver of the Volkswagen, twenty-two-year-old Richard Van Buren, of Onconta, New York, for some reason made a quick turn into what was now the Arundel Arena parking lot. Fleegle's huge tractor clipped him from behind. The Volkswagen spun around and became entangled in the back wheels of

Van Buren's Volkswagen burns as well as the tanker (to the right) as the steel girders of the I-895 bridge start to buckle. (Keith Hammack.)

the tractor and the bottom front of the trailer. The tank trailer, punctured, spewed gasoline as the rig dragged the Volkswagen along with it. The tractor and trailer then skidded and flipped on their sides, coming to rest beneath the north span of the throughway bridge. Miraculously, Fleegle, Van Buren, and Van Buren's passenger, Bertha Birch of Baltimore, made their way out of the wreckage before the tanker exploded. The explosion hurled all three across the parking lot where Arundel Park had burned spectacularly sixteen years before.[15] Again the sky was filled with orange and crimson.

It had been a quiet night in the Anne Arundel County Fire Department communications center, located in the basement of the headquarters building

The partly melted gasoline tanker and attached mangled tractor covered with foam rest harmlessly beneath the heavily damaged I-895 bridge. (Keith Hammack.)

on the northbound lane of Maryland Route 3 in Millersville. The centralized fire alarm dispatch center finally had been established in the wake of the Arundel Park fire, train wrecks, building fires with extraordinary losses, ravaging brush fires, and the hundreds of daily emergency incidents that marked a growing metropolitan county. Now when fire, rescue, or emergency medical services were needed in Anne Arundel County, one no longer had to find the phone book and scan through it to learn which fire department district they were reporting from. As of October 1966 all anyone had to do was dial 987-1212 for North County or 867-1212 for South County (below the South River). The alarm office was in its sixth year of operation and under the command of Division Chief Edwin Utz, who reported to the county fire administrator, Harry Klasmeier.

James "Jimmy" Thomas, an alarm operator when the center first went into operation, had risen to shift lieutenant. On this quiet October night he was in charge of two young firefighters, James Swinimer and Joseph B. Ross Jr., who

With Belle Grove Road to the bridge now covered with high expansion foam, apparatus and equipment park a few feet from the spot where sixteen years earlier eleven lives had been lost. The second generation Arundel Park, the "Arundel Arena" is in the background. Today the building is Bingo World. (Keith Hammack.)

had worked until about 4:00 A.M. Both were asleep in a small map and file room within shouting distance of the alarm center.

As the lights on the telephone switchboard lit and phones began to ring, Jimmy Thomas, manning the fire alarm console, answered one from the county police that reported the tank truck/car crash and fire at the bridge. "Get up! Get up! Get up!" Thomas shouted as he flipped through the company run index cards to dispatch the call over the countywide radio system. Ross and Swinimer, awakened by the lieutenant's raspy, bullhorn of a voice, argued over which one had to get up. Finally Swinimer rose, jumped into his pants, and wandered out to see what had caused all the commotion.

Despite the double multi-tone signals churning out of the Motorola radio base transmitter and opening the radio sets of fire stations across the north end of Anne Arundel County, Ross tried to close his eyes and fall back to sleep. Then he heard Thomas strike the two keys to tone the response and announce into the radio microphone, "Box one-one! Engines 31, 32, 34, Truck 31, and Hi X-1, respond to a gasoline tanker accident and fire on Belle Grove Road at the Harbor Tunnel Throughway Bridge near the Arundel Arena." Ross jumped out of bed and ran to the console.

Fortunately the accident and fire did not kill anyone. Fleegle, Van Buren, and Birch had suffered minor injuries, but that morning all eyes were on the bridge. Within ten minutes of the fire's start, the heat had grown so intense that the large steel I-beams began to buckle and sag.

Police had their hands full. Even with the northbound roadway caving in and the devastating fire beneath them, cars were still trying to cross the damaged bridge. Baltimore commuters did not want to be late for work. Finally, as more officers arrived from the county and the Maryland State Police, tunnel throughway traffic was stopped. Eventually the northbound rush-hour traffic backed up almost eighteen miles to the south along Route 3 in Millersville.

Initially firefighters used heavy water fog streams on the burning gasoline but that proved ineffective and a second alarm was requested. That brought additional equipment and manpower to the scene. Firefighters used a combination attack with protein and high expansion foam to finally control and, hours later, extinguish the fire.

The tractor trailer and Volkswagen, now separated, were blackened, molten wrecks. The bridge remained closed for three months and in the interim the southern span was modified for two-way traffic. Repairs were estimated to have cost between two and three hundred thousand dollars.[16]

On a cold Saturday morning near noon on February 29, 1992, the last standing structure to bear witness to the deadly Arundel Park fire went up in flames. The Matlack Trucking Company office and garage complex at 4801 Belle Grove Road, vacant for a number of years, fell to an arsonist's torch. Once more fire engines lined up along Belle Grove Road. The building was fully involved upon the arrival of the Brooklyn fire engine, a gleaming 1987 enclosed crew cab American Eagle "Spartan" capable of pumping a thousand gallons per minute. The lime yellow engine looked and operated somewhat differently from the red open-cab US pumper that Ed Utz had driven to the Arundel Park fire thirty-six years earlier.

On the cold Saturday morning of February 29, 1992, the vacant Matlack Truck Company building, the last structure to bear witness to the deadly Arundel Park fire, suffered a similar fate. (Keith Hammack.)

The firefighters smartly took a defensive action. With the roof already consumed by the flames, they used their ladder pipes and engine-mounted deluge guns (nozzles) to extinguish the blaze. With additional fire hydrants now located along Belle Grove Road, finding enough water was no longer a challenge. No firefighters were sent inside. Before evening, the three-alarm blaze was completely extinguished. No one was injured. Everyone went home.

13

Memories and Nightmares

On the night of the fire, after she had returned to her 4th Street home from the hospital, a worn out, bandaged, and shaken Lou Sokolis could not sleep. She could only think about the tragedy she had witnessed less than six hours earlier, seeing before her the anguished faces of the families of the women who were still trapped and would never get out. She could not close her eyes for fear of seeing the red and orange flames racing across the ceiling above, or the frightened men who almost killed her, and the one man who inadvertently saved her life.

Lou could still hear the swooshing sound of the flames, the screams and crying inside, the shouting from the outside as relatives called to their missing loved ones, praying and hoping the trapped would hear the sound of their names and find their way outside. Then the masses of struggling, terrified men and women who moments earlier had filled the doors and windows were replaced with black smoke that within seconds turned to raging, bright orange flames. Lou thought they could have been calling and shouting her name from the outside, that she easily could have died in the flames after being knocked to the floor. But she did not die. With pain in her neck and upper back as though someone were repeatedly stabbing her, she struggled back to her feet and fought her way through the smoke and out to the fresh air. She would relive those frightful seconds again and again.

When Lou arrived home, her parents, along with her tired and soot-covered brother Wally, who still smelled of smoke, tried to comfort her, but Lou's mind continued to spin with dreadful thoughts. She felt she had to take a ride with her brother. A ride might help her sort everything out and clear her head. The memory of what happened from the time she was knocked to the floor until she made it to safety played in her mind like a movie endlessly re-run.

After a long ride with her brother, she came back home and walked up the steps to her bedroom, where earlier that morning she had so eagerly looked forward to the oyster roast. The bedroom is where she had combed and brushed her pretty auburn hair, now tangled and matted with the medicated gel and gauze dressings the doctors had applied to the burns on the top of her head. Those earlier, joyous thoughts were millions of miles away. With her brother and mother, who both sat up all night by her side, holding her hands tightly, the exhausted and mentally drained young woman eventually fell asleep.

In the fifty years since that horrible night, Louise Sokolis has thought about the fire every day. It was some time before she could go out to a public gathering. When she did finally acquire the courage to attend functions with large crowds of people, she always sat at the seat or table nearest the exit door. She does so to this day.

Today, Frank Kvech III not only sits near the closest exit, he checks to make sure it is unlocked. He said his father, Frank Jr., would never talk about the fire, even years afterward. Frank said his father was changed. He was very quiet, as though something was bothering him. Frank Jr. might have been thinking about unlocking the latch and pulling up the large overhead door. Perhaps he was trying to sort things out. Why did the fire even happen, and why did it spread so fast? Why couldn't I have made my way to the door more quickly? Couldn't I have disengaged the latching device sooner? Why couldn't those nice ladies I knew from the church get out?[1]

The night after the fire, Frank Jr. along with other church members visited the families of the deceased. It had been a long night for the Baltimore transit worker and member of Saint Rose of Lima Church. Following the fire, he continued to devote most of his free time to church matters, and for the rest of his life he would never talk about the fire with his son, Frank III.

For Harry Zlotowski, an eighteen-year-old volunteer firefighter with the Brooklyn Station, who would later retire as an Anne Arundel County Fire Department division chief with thirty years of service, it was the biggest fire he would ever fight. Even that night he thought, "This is it, this is the big one they all talk about." As he was dragging and positioning hose lines and fighting the fire with some of the same techniques he had learned just that day during class, Harry was unaware that his mother, Cecelia, was inside the building. Fortunately she managed to escape.[2] The only thing Cecelia Zlotowski lost were her shoes, but for the remainder of her life, she would never talk about that night.

Rae (Utz) Bathgate, the wife of Eddie Utz and a member of the Brooklyn Fire Department Ladies Auxiliary, spent most of the evening at the Brooklyn Fire Station making ham, chicken, and bologna sandwiches and coffee for the cold and tired emergency workers. She and the other members of the auxiliary—Thelma Homberg, Mildred Hardy, Jean Helfrich, Leona Zlotowski, Gladys Meseke, Elizabeth Cauliflower, and Marie Schmidt—went down to the fire scene later that night to deliver the food.

To this day Rae has vivid memories of burned shoes, piled in the shape of a pyramid about four feet high, outside the smoking building and wonders what happened to the people who wore them. A couple of days after the fire, Rae wrote a pointed letter to the *Maryland Gazette*, admonishing the sightseers who had interfered with the fire and rescue operations. She basically put them on notice and reminded them that if they want to be part of an emergency operation to get out of the way or work![3]

The son of the Arundel Park fire's hero, Andrew Brady, would pay dearly for that night. According to the Brady family, Andrew Jr. never got over his father's death or the pain he suffered before dying. Although he would later be promoted, become a highly respected detective, and be a candidate to become the chief of police, his life began a downward spiral. For years, hounded by his memories, Andrew Jr. conducted his own unofficial investigation, forever believing that the fire was criminally inspired. That he could never prove his theory only added to his frustrations. As the 1950s passed into the 1960s, Andrew Jr. sparred with life's vices, mainly the demon alcohol, which cost him his marriage. As demons continued to play havoc, he eventually crossed the line. By the mid-1970s, he was involved with a prostitution ring that would cost him still more. Andrew Brady Jr. lost more than his father to the fire; he lost a family and a promising career in law enforcement. He died a broken man in 1998, at the age of seventy-five.[4]

Stella Kozlowski was a friend of my grandmother, Mary Rozmarynowski.

My dad remembers Miss Kozlowski singing in the choir at Saint Adalbert Catholic Church in Wagner's Point not far from Curtis Bay. As a teenager, he played the church organ there and has fond memories of Stella and her sister, Elizabeth Dulaney, singing soprano at mass and at other church events.[5] Later the sisters attended the wedding of my mother and father, which took place at the second Saint Rose of Lima Church building in July 1949. The reception was held at an old, one-story wooden hall that stood where the brick school building stands today.

My dad, as a kid living in Wagner's Point, remembers Stella's brother Johnny stopping at the house on a number of Christmas Eves. As Johnny Kozlowski sipped Christmas cheer with my grandparents, none of them could have known that many years later he would be called into to the Ferndale Police Station after the Arundel Park fire to identify a ring that his sister Stella had so proudly worn.[6]

It was well known to my mom and dad that on Sunday, January 29, 1956, our parish, the Saint Rose of Lima Catholic Church in Brooklyn Holy Name Society, was sponsoring an oyster roast at Arundel Park on Belle Grove Road about a quarter-mile south of our house. Since my grandmother, Mary Rozmarynowski, was very much involved and socialized with a number of people of the church, my father was concerned when alerted to the fire. As fire engines, ambulances, and police cars sped by our little row house on 5th Avenue, my worried father dialed the old rotary telephone to call his brother Stan, who lived with his wife at my grandmother's house on 9th Street in Brooklyn. "Stan, is mom there?" I heard him say. "Stan are you sure? . . . Haven't you heard? . . . The oyster roast is burning!"

"Yes, from seeing all of the ambulances speeding by, apparently a number of people are hurt!" My dad then said "Listen!" and held the phone up and out so Stan could hear the three or four emergency vehicles racing by the house with sirens wailing. This scene in my house was probably occurring in hundreds of households as news of the fire made its way into the warm, modest homes in the Brooklyn area on this cold January evening.

At five years old, I was not really sure what the oyster roast was, but it didn't matter because I jumped up on the living room sofa, pulled the curtains back, and looked out the window. From our end unit one could see the whole intersection of Belle Grove Road and 5th Avenue. I watched and marveled as fire engine after fire engine, ambulance after ambulance, police cars, trucks with red crosses on the side, all with bright red and white flashing lights, rushed down Belle Grove Road.

I then heard my father say, "Thank God! Thank God, they are all right! Thanks, Stan! . . . Stan, Stan, what do you mean? . . . Uncle Frank's there? . . . OK, I'll run down there and see if I can find him!" I then heard my dad telling my mother that his mom and her sister Julia, Uncle Frank's wife, had gone to the movies instead of the oyster roast. But Uncle Frank was at the roast and no one had heard from him.

I can still remember my dad, a veteran World War II fighter pilot, putting on his old Army Air Corps jacket with the fur around the collar, rushing out the back door of the house, and walking very quickly up the hill that led to the Belle Grove Elementary School yard. I ran back upstairs and through the bathroom window watched him walk across the school's playground in the direction of the flames, the whole time wishing that he had taken me.

It was getting dark, and I soon lost sight of him. I then watched the fire engines working at the hydrant at 5th Avenue and Belle Grove Road. The vacant lot between the alley beside my house and Belle Grove Road was filling up with cars and groups of people, all walking and running along Belle Grove Road toward the fire.

Not long after my dad left, my mother, who had the television turned on, directed my attention to the special bulletin that was on the little twelve-inch screen. The black and white picture showed a video shot of the front of the building, which I recognized as the bingo building that I had ridden past in my dad's car many times and had been inside only a week before.

I remembered driving down to Arundel Park with my mom's sister, my Aunt Rae, and their brother, my Uncle Jack, who was only five years older than I was. My mom was pregnant with my younger brother Jerry and had a craving for a milkshake and a cheeseburger. So Aunt Rae, who would do anything for her older sister, put Jack and me in the car and drove down to Arundel Park. While we waited for the milkshake and the cheeseburger in the milk bar, Aunt Rae played the big "one-armed bandit" slot machine that was up against a wall near the huge opening into the main hall. I can't remember if she won any money. My Uncle Jack sat on the red vinyl seat of one of the soda bar stools and spun himself around, and I stood in the big doorway watching all the people play bingo in the main hall. A week later this major exit doorway through the milk bar from the main hall would be closed and padlocked the evening of the fire.

Now as I watched the fire on the television set, I was wondering if the big, multi-colored, neon sign on the Belle Grove Road side of the building would survive. The sign always fascinated me when we drove by in my dad's big 1949 Plymouth. The lights seemed to spin in a circle, like a large pinwheel. I used to think that it was a lighted wheel with colored lights that revolved around and around.

An hour or so later my dad, Uncle Frank Spiegel, and a family friend, Walter Halleck, walked through the front door. I think my mom hugged them or something, but I'm not really sure. They were still neatly dressed with white shirts and ties but no jackets or coats. I remember pestering my Uncle Frank for all the details. He just very politely and calmly, which was his way, said that the lights had gone out and he had climbed out a window.[7] When I was older and had become interested in fires and the fire department, I would ask Uncle Frank for his recollections of that night, but all he'd ever say was that the lights had gone out and he had climbed out a window—nothing more, nothing less.

The Saturday morning after the fire, my dad drove my mom, my little brother Jimmy, and me to the fire site. It was raining as we slowly drove across the parking lot and around the building. We could see a thick barricade rope encircling what was left of the structure to keep people away. The once white concrete block walls had black scorch marks around the tops where the roof had been and around what was left of the windows. The formerly red and white metal awnings were collapsed against the building or on the ground. Inside nothing was left but ashes and burned timbers. I had no idea that a fire could be so destructive.

The big electric neon sign was nowhere to be found and must have been consumed in the flames. I would find out years later that the fire inside the building had reached temperatures of 1,860 degrees Fahrenheit, hot enough to melt glass. As my dad drove around to the back of the building, I remember my mom saying this is where the kitchen was and the fire started from grease. I didn't really understand what she was talking about, but she was my mom so I didn't question her comment.

The following spring, my father took me for long walks. He said he needed the exercise, but since I was something of a hyperactive child, I

Guests at the wedding of Joe and Peg Ross in July 1949 include Elizabeth Dulaney (front row, second from right) and next to her in the polka dot dress is her sister, Stella Kozlowski, who did not survive the fire. Elizabeth's husband, James Dulaney, is in the top row, fourth from right. (Author's collection.)

think he just walked me to wear me out so I would go to bed early. On one particular Sunday, we walked down to what was left of Arundel Park. The walls had been pulled down and the debris picked up and hauled away. All that remained of the building were the tops of the eight-inch concrete blocks that protruded from the ground about six inches and outlined the entire perimeter of where the building had once stood. The scorched concrete floor was still there, but it had been swept clean.

I remember sitting on one of the concrete blocks, wondering whatever happened to the "one-armed bandit" that my Aunt Rae played, while my dad walked around looking at the few remaining traces of what had once been northern Anne Arundel County's largest covered-floor area for public use. Eventually, all of the remains were dug up and the place covered with asphalt. About a year later construction started on a new building that sits farther back toward the woods than the original, which had been very close to Belle Grove Road. The new one, renamed the Arundel Arena for many years after, is still there today and is now the Bingo World. As a kid I was never excited about the new building because it didn't have all the colorful revolving neon lights.

The oyster roast was supposed to be an afternoon of fun, an opportunity to have a good time with loved ones, relatives, and friends. By 5:00 P.M. it would have been over in an hour. Under very different circumstances, everyone would have gone home with new friends, prizes, a couple of extra bucks, fond memories, and smiles on their faces. They would have returned to warm houses, watched Ed Sullivan on the television, kissed their children good night, turned in, and the next morning gone to their jobs in factories, rail yards, offices, shops, at construction sites, and on the waterfront, or stayed home to take care of the kids.

It is hard to imagine that in a span of three minutes so many bad things happened to change the lives of so many good people forever. Three minutes—the time it takes to count to one hundred and eighty. Only three minutes elapsed from the time the fire burst through the huge ceiling until the Brooklyn engine arrived and found the entire interior engulfed in flames.

One hundred and eighty seconds. Count them, and while you're counting, close your eyes and try to visualize everything you just read.

Epilogue

More than fifty years have passed since the Arundel Park fire. We know that, for the most part, preventive measures before the fire, responses to it, and three investigations afterward were all undertaken in the most reasonable, professional, and ethical manner, given the state of knowledge and the experience of those in authority at the time. Almost every known safety measure was taken. A fire inspection was performed in March 1955, almost nine months before the tragedy, during which everything relating to fire and safety was found to be in order. A comprehensive investigation ruled out any connections to organized crime and correctly concluded that the fire started in the kitchen ceiling with an electrical short or a spark from the fireplace.

There was one glaring exception: Arundel Park had no automatic sprinkler system. A chance to enforce that requirement was lost at the time the structure was built. We will never know why that opportunity was squandered. An automatic sprinkler system installed throughout the massive structure would have profoundly changed the evening of January 29, 1956.

Arundel Park was directly responsible for the safety of the twelve hundred people who attended the oyster roast. Its managers should have made certain that patrons evacuated immediately, even when their most junior member learned of the fire. Management should have called the fire department. The exit doors never should have been padlocked shut. The locked doors were in violation of the county fire code and contradicted all common sense. It also strains credulity that the approximately twenty career and volunteer firefighters attending or working the event that evening either did not notice the locked double exit doors between the hall and the milk bar, or, if they did notice, failed to force management to correct the problem.

Had these shortcomings been addressed the Arundel Park fire might have been a success story after a close call and not the striking tragedy it became. As it was, eleven people died, more than 250 others were injured, and we will never know how many more were, like Andrew Brady Jr., psychologically scarred. In the 1950s, little information was available on the effects of post-traumatic stress.

But clearly the biggest contributor to the disaster was the highly combustible fibercane or celotex tile used in construction of the ceiling. After numerous fires throughout the nation, especially that which killed the school children in Buffalo, New York, the dangerous tile should have been removed from the marketplace and from every building in which it had been installed.

Today, there is no memorial, no flag, no plaque, nothing to remind people of that terrible Sunday evening in January 1956. An asphalt-covered parking lot marks the site where Mrs. Frances Cooke and Miss Stella Kozlowski and eight other wonderful people lost their lives. In many ways it is hallowed ground, a place where heroism overcame fear, where Andrew Brady unselfishly performed his last final act of public service. It is where brave men and women rose to fight an impossible fire. When they couldn't control it they tried to maintain calm amidst mounting panic, forced open huge overhead doors, broke through other doors that should never have been locked, and smashed out windows, all so that others might escape. All but ten of those twelve hundred did.

Perhaps the greatest lesson to be learned from Arundel Park is that we must remain vigilant. A number of those in the hall saw what was going on around them, and acted wisely. When they saw men running with fire extinguishers and smoke puffing from the ceiling, they did not hesitate but followed their instincts and got out, whether they were laughed at or not. Some even had time to pick up their coats and wraps from the cloak room before they departed.

A similar pattern appeared on September 11, 2001, when office workers in the South Tower of New York's World Trade Center took matters into their own hands. Moments after the hijacked jet struck the North Tower, those in the South Tower began evacuating their building. Fearing that they might be struck by debris and bodies falling from the North Tower, authorities directed them back to their offices. Following their instincts, many disregarded the directive and got out anyway. Many of those who obeyed and reoccupied the upper floors were killed or injured when the second plane crashed into the South Tower minutes later.[1]

If there is one lesson of the many to be learned and remembered here, it is vigilance. Today, with most buildings constructed of non-combustible building materials and protected by automatic sprinkler systems, automatic smoke detection, and fire alarm systems connected to elaborate 911 systems, it would be easy to take fire protection and safety for granted. Yet the countless fire tragedies that have occurred throughout the nation over the past fifty years and the recent destructive fires in buildings protected by automatic sprinkler systems prove that we are not totally safe. It is up to us as citizens to question authorities, and to ask about unsafe conditions and the lack of such things as sprinklers, detectors, and alarms in the buildings we use.

While we are about our daily activities, whether at work or play, we must be vigilant. We must be aware of dangerous conditions and behavior in our surroundings. Periodically we should ask ourselves, "If something goes wrong here, how can I and those with me, get out?" All of us must do everything humanly possible to prevent tragic events from happening again. Fire safety is just not the responsibility of the fire department. It is a partnership involving the fire department, schools and businesses, and people of the community. The partnership will keep us and our loved ones safe from fire today and tomorrow, providing we all do our part.

Appendix A

Computing public assembly capacity

The capacity of the Arundel Park as well as other public assembly occupancies was determined by dividing the total floor area (in square feet) expected to be occupied by the attending public by ten, the number of square feet used per person. The resulting number (of people) is then compared to a second number, the number of exit doors providing at least twenty-two inches of clear exit width for every one hundred persons expected to exit per minute in an emergency. If the aggregate of all the exit doors produces an occupant load less than the load based on square footage, the lower figure serves as the occupant load. (Today, the Life Safety Code requires fifteen square feet per person to reduce the number of people attending an indoor assembly to a safer level.)[26]

The Arundel Park met all of the occupant load and exit requirements based on the old (ten square feet) standard as well as today's. The capacity for Arundel Park was 1,500 people, which included the floor area in the milk bar and cocktail lounge in addition to the main hall.[27]

Fire Extinguishers

Arundel Park was equipped with two types of portable fire extinguishers. One type, soda and acid, extinguishes by cooling the fire with water. Mounted to the wall, the cylindrical three-foot long, shiny container was characterized by its metal "crown," usually painted blue. To activate it, the operator inverts the extinguisher and sets the eight-inch diameter cylinder down on the floor/ground supported by the "crown." A small glass bottle secured inside the lightly walled metal container disengages its lead cap and a small amount of sulfuric acid is discharged into two and a half gallons of bicarbonate water solution, creating carbon dioxide gas. This gas immediately compresses the solution, forcing it through a small rubber hose attached to a plastic nozzle held by the operator and aimed at the fire. Soda and acid extinguishers were considered acceptable and were given a Class A rating by the Insurance Rating Bureaus. Though bulky and slightly heavy, they worked fairly well if maintained properly and serviced once a year and were capable of projecting a stream of water up to about twenty feet for a limited time.

The Class A rated extinguisher was only approved for small fires involving paper, cardboard, clothing, wood, trash, and other ordinary combustibles. Five Soda and Acid extinguishers were mounted and unobstructed on the walls throughout the facility.[28] Because failures of the thin cylinder wall caused dangerous ruptures of the shell, soda and acid extinguishers were phased out in the mid-1970s and are today illegal.

The other type of fire extinguisher at Arundel Park was the carbon dioxide type. This extinguisher with its cylindrical container made of a heavy gauged steel and painted red with a hard rubber insulated hose attached to a nozzle, was filled with ten pounds of liquid carbon dioxide (CO2). The liquid compressed in the cylinder turned into a gas when dispersed into the atmosphere.

Unlike the soda and acid extinguisher, the CO2 did not have to be inverted. A trigger similar to that of a garden hose was mounted on the top of the cylinder and an attached hard rubber hose. The hose was attached to a plastic/rubber cone-shaped nozzle, by which the operator directed the cold expanding white colored gas at the flames. Upon discharge, the pressurized CO2 gas spiraling around in the plastic cone created a distinctive sound, like a muted fog-horn, when the agent was dispersed.

The CO2 extinguisher under extreme pressure releases an inert gas which smothers the fire by eliminating its oxygen. This Class BC rated extinguisher was very effective on small grease and liquid fuel fires and fires involving energized electrical equipment. The facility had three CO2 extinguishers, two of which were mounted in the kitchen. The service tags also indicated they were checked in 1955. CO2 extinguishers are still in use today.

Appendix B

Diagram of the Arundel Park

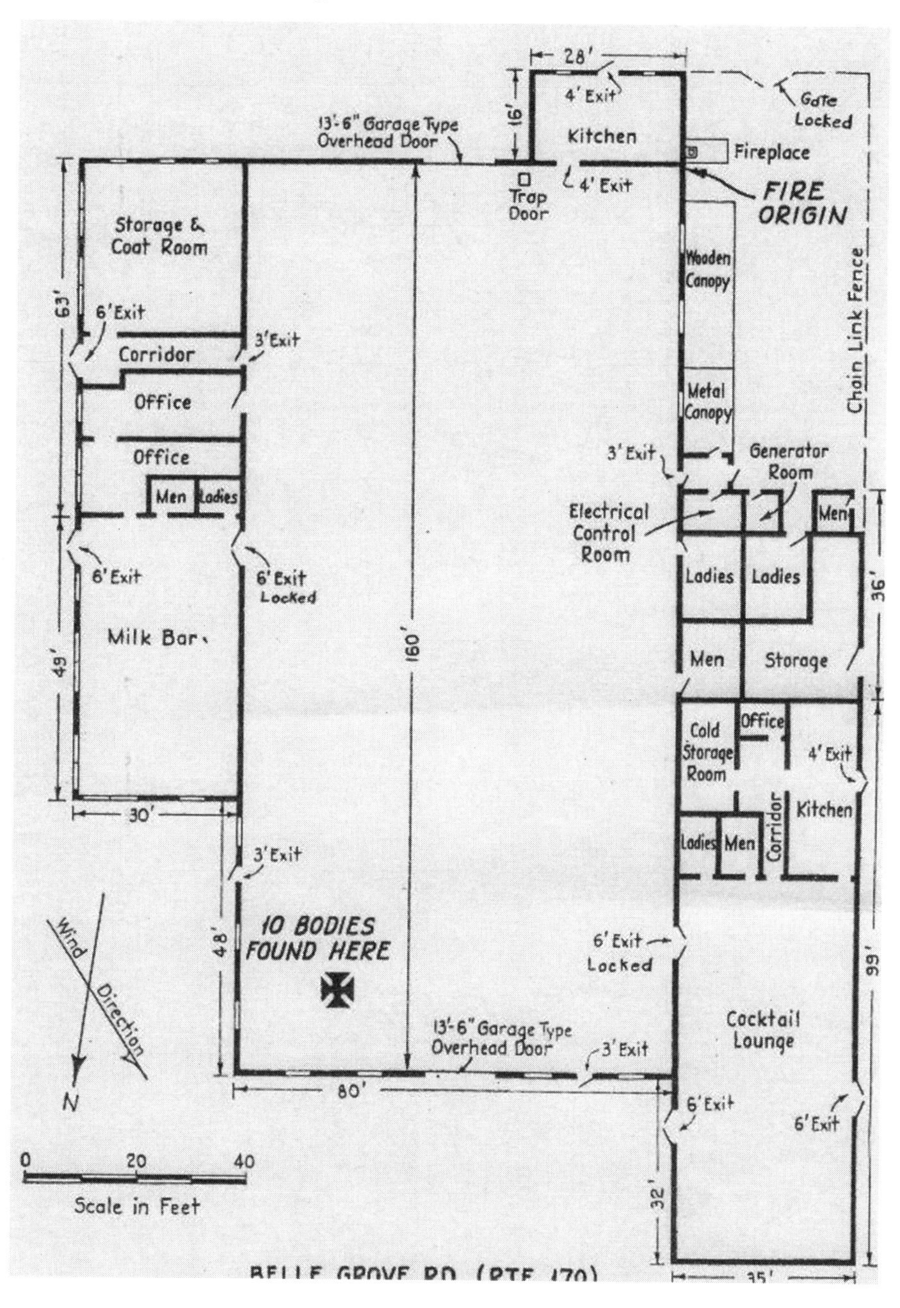

Reprinted with permission from the NFPA Quarterly, April 1956.

Appendix C — Fire Operations Map

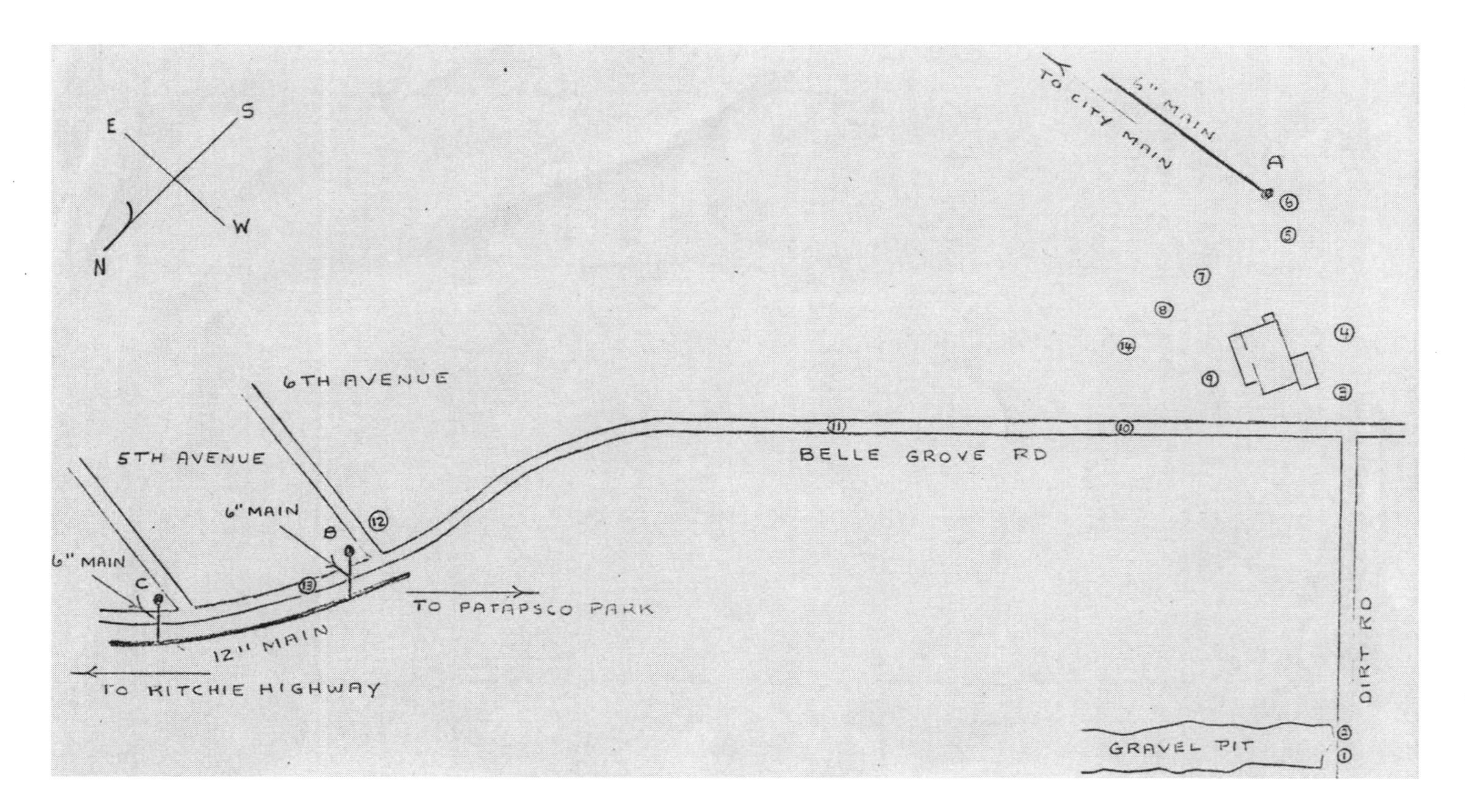

Anne Arundel County Fire Marshal Harry Klasmeier's original drawing and notes (opposite page) of fire operations at Arundel Park, January 29, 1956, from the Fire Investigation Task Force.

KEY TO DIAGRAM

0 HYDRANT

(1) HYDRANT A
TYPE-MATHEWS-THREE WAY-on 6 inch water main
DISTANCE TO BUILDING-300 feet

(2) HYDRANT-B
TYPE-MATHEWS-THREE WAY-on 6 inch water main
DISTANCE TO BUILDING-2,000 feet

(3) HYDRANT C
TYPE-MATHEWS-THREE WAY_on 6 inch water main
DISTANCE TO BUILDING-2,530 feet

O-PUMPER

1. Glen Burnie-Engine #3--750 Gallon Pumper
2. Linthicum-Engine #1--500 Gallon Pumper
3. Earleigh Heights-Engine #1--750 Gallon Pumper
4. Earleigh Heights-Engine #2--500 Gallon Pumper
5. Brooklyn Engine #1--750 Gallon Pumper
6. Brooklyn Engine #2--750 gallon Pumper
7. Ferndale Engine #2--750 Gallon Pumper
8. Marley Engine #2--500 Gallon Pumper
9. Orchard Beach Engine #3--750 Gallon Pumper
10. Riviera Beach Engine #3--750 Gallon Pumper
11. Glen Burnie Engine #1--750 Gallon Pumper and Service Ladder Truck
12. Riviera Beach Engine #2--600 Gallon Pumper
13. Green Haven Engine #2--500 Gallon Pumper
14. Powhatan Beach Engine #2--500 Gallon Pumper

OTHER PUMPERS AT SCENE WERE LOCATED AROUND BUILDING AND CREWS AIDED.

MANNING HOSE LINE SUPPLYING HOSE, RESCUE AND SALVAGE OPERATIONS:

PUMPING OPERATIONS:

1. Glen Burnie Engine #3
   a. Taking suction from gravel pit supplied one 2½ inch line to the fire.
2. Linthicum Engine #1
   b. Two taking suction from gravel pit supplied one 2½ inch line to the fire.
3. Brooklyn Engine #2
   c. 6 taking suction from hydrant "A" supplied 3-2½ inch lines to Brooklun Engine #1.
   5 Brooklyn Engine #1 supplied 2-2½ inch line was supplied from Brooklyn Engine #1 to Ferndale Engine #2.
   7 Ferndale Engine #2 supplied 2-1½ inch lines directly to the fire.
4. Riviera Beach Engine #2-12 taking suction from hydrant "B" supplied 2-2½ inch lines to Glen Burnie Engine #1.
   11 Glen Burnie Engine #1 supplied 1-2½ inch line to Riviera Beach Engine #3. Riviera Beach Engine #3 (10) supplied 2 1½ inch lines directly to the fire and 1-2½ inch line to Earleigh Heights Engine #1. (3) Earleigh Heights Engine #1 supplied 2-1½ inch line directly to the fire and 1-2½ inch line to Earleigh Heights Engine #2. (4) Earleigh Heights Engine #2 supplied 1-2½ inch line directly to the fire. A second 2½ inch line supplied from Glen Burnie Engine #1 to Orchard Beach Engine #3. Orchard Beach Engine #3 (9) supplied 3-1½ inch lines directly to the fire.

5. Green Haven Engine #2 (13) operated 1-2½ inch line from hydrant "C" and supplied Powhatan Beach Engine #2 (14) who shuttled tank loads of water to Marley Engine #2. Marley Engine #2 supplied 1-1½ inch line directly to the fire.

All firefighting and rescue operations were under the direction of Chief Joseph Neil of the Brooklyn Community Fire Company.

Appendix D

BUILDING CODE EVALUATION
OF THE ARUNDEL PARK
CONSTRUCTED IN BROOKLN PARK, MARYLAND
IN 1948

The object of this paper is to determine if the Arundel Park, constructed in 1948, was in compliance with the Anne Arundel County Building Code regarding fire protection requirements.

Facts

The Anne Arundel County Building Code was enacted on March 14, 1939, approximately nine years before the construction of Arundel Park. It required the following:

Article 1, Section 100. Scope 4. *All new work to conform.* (a) No building or structure shall hereafter be constructed, altered, repaired or removed, nor shall the equipment of a building, structure or premises be constructed, installed, altered, repaired or removed, except in conformity with the provisions of the Building Code.

Section 404. Area Limitations 1. *New Buildings.* No building hereafter erected shall exceed in areas in any story above grade, limits fixed by this section.

7. *Ordinary Construction.* Ordinary-construction shall not exceed 5,000 square feet for buildings fronting on one street, 6,000 square feet for buildings fronting two streets, nor 7,500 square feet fronting on three or more streets.

8. *Area Modification.* (a.) The limiting areas fixed in this section may be increased by one hundred percent when the building is sprinklered, and by

two hundred percent when the building is sprinklered and does not exceed one story nor an average of twenty-five feet in height to the roof or to a ceiling which is unpierced and has a fire resistance of not less then one hour.

(b.) Outside the fire limits, when a hazardous condition is not created thereby, the area of a public-building, a business building or a storage building, not over two stories high, may be increased in excess of the areas fixed by this section, in the discretion of a board consisting of the President of the Board of County Commissioners, the building official and the chief of the fire department which protects the territory in which the building is to be erected; providing that buildings of combustible occupancy shall be sprinklered.

Area of Arundel Park:

Main Hall	12,800 sq. ft.
Cocktail Lounge/Storage/Restrooms	3,465 sq. ft.
Milk Bar/Offices/Storage/Coat Room	3,360 sq. ft.
Kitchen	448 sq. ft.
Total	20,073 sq. ft.

Situation
The area of Arundel Park was 20,073 sq ft.

Since the main hall was constructed in 1948 and the other entities were added on later, the main hall will be the focus of this paper.

Ordinary Construction was limited to 5,000 sq ft for buildings fronting one street. Since the building only fronted one street, Belle Grove Road, it would be (12,800 – 5,000) 7,800 sq. ft. over the one street limitation.

The Arundel Park main hall building was constructed at an angle to Belle Grove, making it possible to receive the 2 street credit. The 2 street condition limited the building to 6,000 sq. ft. still resulting in (12,800 – 6,000) 6,800 sq. ft. over the two street limitation.

The maximum area for Ordinary Construction was 7,000 sq. ft. providing the building fronted more than three streets. Considering Arundel Park had access (parking lot) on at least 3 sides and complied with the 3 street limitation it was still (12,800 – 7,000) 5,800 sq. ft. over the three street limitation.

Requirement #9. Area Modification allows the Arundel Park to be increased by 100% if the building is protected by an automatic sprinkler system. This provision would allow the building to be erected with a 10,000 sq. ft. limitation. Even under this consideration the building was still (12,800 – 10,000) 2,800 sq. ft. over the limit. Or 12,000 sq. ft. (6,000 x 2) with the 2 street credit or 14,000 sq. ft. (7,000 x 2) with the 3 street credit.

The Arundel Park meeting the 3 street credit would be a stretch because of the questionability of meeting the 3 streets requirement technically. But if that requirement was waved due to the parking lot accessibility the area, would be limited to 14,000 sq. ft.

The building would still be required to have an automatic sprinkler system at 12,800 sq. ft. to be in compliance with the code.

In applying the (b.) outside the fire-limits requirement, the building may be increased in excess of the areas fixed by the section providing:

> they are not over two stories and,
>
> in the discretion of the President of the Board of County Commissioners, the building official and the chief of the of the fire department which protects the territory in which the building is to be erected and,
>
> buildings of combustible occupancy shall be sprinklered.

In the Building Code "fire-limits" is defined as territory or those districts within Anne Arundel County, exclusive of the City of Annapolis, described in this Building Code, in which, with certain specified exceptions, frame-construction and unprotected-metal-construction are prohibited.

Considering the other types of construction built up and down the Belle Grove Road corridor at the time, the location of the Arundel Park was not likely to lie within a fire-limit, later called fire districts by the BOCA Building Code.

In applying the "Outside the fire limits" requirement, the building could be constructed if it was under two stories, which it was. And in agreement with the President of the Board of County Commissioners, the building inspector, and the Brooklyn Park fire chief (which there is no record of the three principles agreeing or not). And most important "that buildings of combustible occupancy shall be sprinklered." (whatever that means)

Since there is no definition of "combustible occupancy" in the building code it can only be left to interpretation. Other then the concrete block walls, all other materials (such as the wooden ceiling truss, the wooden roof, and the fiberboard ceiling tile) were combustible. It would have been rather simple to classify the Arundel Park as a "combustible occupancy."

Findings

The requirements on area limitations set in the code are clear on establishing automatic sprinkler requirements for Ordinary Construction areas exceeding 5,000 to 14,000 square feet. Yet when areas exceed the 14,000 maximum, the code left the interpretation decision to laymen, who may or may not have the experience, training or knowledge to make serious code interpretations – it is mind boggling.

Based on the facts and situation presented, for all practicality, the Arundel Park, under the 1939 building code, was required to be protected by an automatic sprinkler system. Not having a system, the building was approved for construction and occupied illegally.

Appendix E

The Arundel Park fire was not the first fire disaster to strike a public event sponsored by a Catholic Church organization, and neither was it the worst. Most sadly, though, it would also not be the last.

In January 1942, in Saint Johns, Newfoundland, five hundred people were attending a barn dance at a Knights of Columbus hall when a fire broke out. As was the case with Arundel Park, the fire was soon thought to be under control. The first warning came at 11:00 P.M. and was announced in a radio show that was being broadcast from the facility. Shortly after that announcement reported the fire to be under control, the blaze sprang up, followed by a stampede to the exits. By the time firefighters arrived from the station only two hundred yards away, the building was described as having become a roaring mass of flames. The fire resulted in 104 dead and 130 injured, mainly World War II servicemen. Most of the bodies were found near exits where dozens had been trampled.*

On May 23, 1964, the All Hollows Catholic Church was holding a fund raiser at its small (one hundred by fifty feet) single-story wooden hall in San Francisco. The fund raiser was a variety show consisting of several acts, the final being a Samoan Flaming Sword Dance. Disregarding fire code regulations and defying all common sense, the dancer placed a pan containing roughly one gallon of gasoline on the stage. The dancer was supposed to first dip the sword into the gasoline and then ignite it with two lit candles that were also on the stage. Apparently, before the dancer could ignite his sword, someone flicked a cigarette lighter, which accidentally ignited the gasoline fumes and an instant later the entire pan of flammable liquid.

Seeing the fire, a stage hand activated a pressurized water fire extinguisher to suppress it. Since flammable liquids are lighter and float on top of water, the water spread the fire across the stage and onto the stage curtains as the audience just stared in amazement. In a few seconds the fire had climbed up the curtains and touched off the combustible fiberboard ceiling tile. Flames

* "St. Johns, Newfoundland," Fire Engineering, January 1942, 23.

swept across the ceiling, much as they had at the oyster roast fire eight years earlier on the other side of the continent. The crowd panicked, upending tables and knocking over chairs and made a mad rush to the front entrance. When it was all over, five people had been trapped and burned to death. Eighty-two others had been injured before escaping. A total of seventeen died from burns. Many who tried to escape were hindered by people trying to get back inside and help with the evacuation. The catastrophe was all too familiar.*

2. "San Francisco Social Hall Fire," *Quarterly of the National Fire Protection Association* (October 1964): 103.

References

Introduction
1. Anne Arundel County Police Department, Anne Arundel County Fire Prevention Bureau, Maryland State Police [combined report]. Report of the Arundel Park Fire. 1956.

Prologue
1. Anne Arundel County Police Department, Anne Arundel County Fire Prevention Bureau, Maryland State Police [combined report]. Report of the Arundel Park Fire. 1956.
2. Bruno, Hal. "Relearning Old Lessons From a Night Club Tragedy," *Firehouse*. New York, New York: March 2006. p.18.

Chapter 1: A Community and a River
1. William A. Murray, *The Unheralded Heroes of Baltimore's Big Blazes: A Story about Baltimore Firefighters* (Baltimore: E. J. Schmitz & Sons, Inc., 1969), 43–48.
2. Ibid., p. 154.
3. Paul Robert Lyons, *Fire in America!* (Boston : National Fire Protection Association, 1976,) 116, 180–83.
5. Interview with Frank Homberg Jr., 2005.
6. Henry K. Sharp, *The Patapsco River Valley: Cradle of the Industrial Revolution in Maryland* (Baltimore: Maryland Historical Society, 2001).
7. Paul J. Travers, *The Patapsco: Baltimore's River of History* (Centreville, Md.: Tidewater Publishers, 1990), 3.
8. Daniel Carroll Toomey, *A History of Relay Maryland and the Thomas Viaduct* (Baltimore: Toomey Press, 1984), 7.
9. Interview with Charlie Doegen, 2005.
10 Jack Kelbaugh, "The History of Ritchie Highway," *Anne Arundel County History Notes*, 28 (October 1997).
11. Ibid.
12. *Remember When* (Millersville, Tenn.: Seek Publishing, 1956).
13. Interview with Loretta Kane Dove, 2006.
14. *A History of Curtis Bay and Brooklyn* (Brooklyn, Md.: Brooklyn-Curtis Bay Bicentennial Committee, 1976).
15. Ibid.
16. Ibid.
17. Ibid.
18. Interview with Loretta Kane Dove, 2006.
19. *History of Curtis Bay and Brooklyn.*
20. Interview with Loretta Kane Dove, 2006.
21. Ibid.
22. Interview with Michael Ripnick, 2006.
23. Interview with Loretta Kane Dove, 2006.
24. Ibid.
25. *Report of the Arundel Park Fire*, [Combined report of the Anne Arundel County Police Department, Anne Arundel County Fire Prevention Bureau, Maryland State Police], 1956. [Hereafter cited as *Combined Report.*]
26. Ibid.
27. Interview with Michael Ripnick, 2006.
28. "Church Supper Fire—Panic Brings Death to 11, Injuries Over 200," *Fire Engineering*, April 1956, 315.
29. Advertisement in [Glen Burnie, Maryland] *Brooklyn News*, January 19, 1956.
30. *Combined Report.*.
31. Anne Arundel County Building Code, March 1939.

Chapter 2: Suppression, Training, and Inspection
1. NFPA Handbook, 18th ed. (Quincy,

Mass.: National Fire Protection Association, 1997), 1–8.
2. NFPA Handbook, 13th ed. (Quincy, Mass.: National Fire Protection Association, 1969), 1–59.
3. Murray, *Unheralded Heroes*, 77.
4. "Brooklyn Fireman Recalls — Horses Borrowed, Fighters Came Running at Arundel Dept.," [Glen Burnie] *Maryland Gazette,* 1960.
5. *History of Curtis Bay and Brooklyn.*
6. Murray, *Unheralded Heroes*, 77, 87.
7. "Firefighting Bug Hit Neil Early — Lived Near Firehouse," [Glen Burnie] *Maryland Gazette*, 1960.
8. Norman E. Ray Jr., "Brooklyn Community Volunteer Fire Company Inc.: The Early Years, 1936–1942," 2002, 1.
9. "Brooklyn Fire Unit Grows; Adds Truck," [Glen Burnie] *Maryland Gazette,* ca. 1960.
10. Ray, *Brooklyn Community Volunteer Fire Company,* 1.
11. Ibid., 1, 3.
12. *History of Curtis Bay and Brooklyn.*
13. Ray, *Brooklyn Community Volunteer Fire Company,* 2.
14. Ibid., 6.
15. "Service-Members' Readjustment Act of 1944," http://www.gibill.va.gov/GI_Bill_Info/history.htm.
16. Maryland Gazette, January 5, 1956. The Arundel Park fire would be the airport fire department's first response into the county under the new agreement.
17. "10 Die, 250 Hurt as Hall Burns in Brooklyn," *Baltimore Evening Sun*, January 30, 1956.
18. Interview with Charles Doegen, 2005.
19. Interview with Les Helfrich, 2006.
20. Interview with Harry Klasmeier, 2005.
21. "19 Anne Arundel County Schools Branded as Fire Traps," *Baltimore News-Post.* February 8, 1956.
22. Murray, *Unheralded Heroes*, 123.
23. Interview with Harry Klasmeier, 2005.
24. *Fire Prevention Code of Anne Arundel County,* 1952.
25. Interview with Harry Klasmeier, 2005.
26. Harry Klasmeier, "Arundel Park – Fire Prevention Bureau Report," Annapolis, March 12, 1955.
27. Ibid.
28. Interview with Harry Klasmeier, 2005.
29. Interview with Brady, Thompson, and Feeley, 2008.

Chapter 3: A Church Emerges from the Ashes

1. *History of Curtis Bay and Brooklyn.*
2. "History of Saint Rose of Lima," 2003, http://www.stroseparish.org/history.htm, 4.
3. Ibid.
4. Ibid.
5. Murray, *Unheralded Heroes.*
6. "History of Saint Rose of Lima,"
7. Interview with Brady, Thompson, and Feeley, 2008.
8. Ibid.
9. "Arundel Park Fire Hero Is Eleventh Victim," *Baltimore Sun,* February 5, 1956.
10. Interview with Brady, Thompson, and Feeley, 2008.
11. Ibid.
12. "History of Saint Rose of Lima,"
13. Ibid.
14. Ibid.
15. Ibid.
16. *Brooklyn News,* June 13, 1956.
17. "Weather Bureau Report," *Baltimore News-Post.* January 27, 1956.
18. Thomas P. Brophy and Abe Bearnhardt, "Report on Investigation of Fire at Arundel Park, Anne Arundel County, Maryland," private investigation report for Arundel Park Corporation, February 15, 1956. [Hereafter cited as Brophy Report.]
19. Interview with Loretta Kane Dove, 2006.

Chapter 4: Oysters, Beer, and Games of Chance

1. *Catholic Review.* February 3, 1956.
2. "The Strike," editorial, *Baltimore Sun,,* January 30, 1956

3. Interview with Les Helfrich, 2006.
4. Fire Service Extension. *Firemen's Basic.* University of Maryland., College Park, Maryland: 1961.
5. Interview with Frank Homberg Jr., 2005.
6. "Brooklyn News," *Maryland Gazette,* January 19, 1956.
7. *Combined Report of the Arundel Park Fire*, 6.
8. Ibid., 6.
9. Ibid., 6.
10. Interview with Frank Kvech III, 2006.
11. *Catholic Review.* January 20, 1956.
12. "The Strike," *Baltimore Sun,* January 30, 1956.
13. Interview with Brady, Thompson and Feeley, 2008.
14. Ibid.
15. Ibid.
16. Ibid.
17. *Combined Report of the Arundel Park Fire*, 6.
18. *Remember When 1955.* Millersville, TN: Seek Publishing.
19. *Combined Report of the Arundel Park Fire*, 9.
20. Interview with Frank Kvech, III, 2006.
21. *Combined Report of the Arundel Park Fire*, 9.
22. Interview with Brady, Thompson and Feeley, 2008.
23. Interview with Loretta Kane Dove, 2006; 24. R. E. Stevens, "Church Oyster Roast Fire Panic," *Quarterly of the National Fire Protection Association,* 49 (1956): 280.

Chapter 5: Fatal Delay
1. Interview with Harry Zlotowski, 2005.
2. *Combined Report of the Arundel Park Fire,* 10.
3. Brophy Report, 10.
4. *Combined Report of the Arundel Park Fire,* 10–11.
5. Ibid., 11.
6. D. Cowan, and J. Kuenster, *To Sleep With Angels: The Story of a Fire* (Chicago: Ivan R. Dee, 1996), 29, 34.
7. Ibid., 172.
8. R. Lawson, R. *Beverly Hills Supper Club: The Anatomy of a Nightclub Fire* (Athens: Ohio University Press, 1984), 250.
9. Stevens, "Church Oyster Roast Fire Panic," 280.
10. Brophy Report, 14.
11. *Combined Report of the Arundel Park Fire*, 10.
12. Ibid., p. 11.
13. Ibid.
14. "10 Dead in Fire Here, 250 Hurt as Crowd Panics," *Baltimore News-Post,* January 30, 1956.
15. Interview with Frank Kvech III, 2006.
16. *Combined Report of the Arundel Park Fire,* 11.
17. "10 Dead in Fire Here, 250 Hurt as Crowd Panics," *Baltimore News-Post,* January 30, 1956.
18. "Church Supper Fire—Panic Brings Death to 11, Injuries Over 200," 346.
19. "10 Dead in Fire Here, 250 Hurt as Crowd Panics," *Baltimore News-Post,* January 30, 1956.
20. Brophy Report, 8, 15.
21. "Church Supper Fire—Panic Brings Death to 11, Injuries Over 200," 346.
22. "Not All Were Heroes, Nor Did All Panic," *Baltimore Evening Sun,* January 30, 1956.

Chapter 6: Fire, Panic, and Escape
1. *Combined Report of the Arundel Park Fire,* 12.
2. Interview with Frank Kvech Jr., 2006.
3. Interview with Brady, Thompson & Feeley, 2008.
4. *Combined Report of the Arundel Park Fire*, 12.
5. "10 Dead in Fire Here, 250 Hurt as Crowd Panics," *Baltimore News-Post,* January 30, 1956.
6. *Combined Report of the Arundel Park Fire*, 13.
7. "10 Dead in Fire Here, 250 Hurt as Crowd Panics," *Baltimore News-Post,* January 30, 1956.

8. Stevens, "Church Oyster Roast Fire Panic," 281.
9. "Women Knocked Down and Trampled in Fire," *Baltimore News-Post,* January 30, 1956.
10. Ibid.
11. "10 Dead in Fire Here, 250 Hurt as Crowd Panics," *Baltimore News-Post,* January 30, 1956.
12. "Not All Were Heroes, Nor Did All Panic," *Baltimore Evening Sun,* January 30, 1956.
13. "Survivor Says Hall Burned Like Egg Crate," *Baltimore News-Post.* January 30, 1956.
14. "10 Dead in Fire Here, 250 Hurt as Crowd Panics," *Baltimore News-Post,* January 30, 1956.
15. Ray, *Brooklyn Community Volunteer Fire Company Inc.,* 3.
16. "10 Dead in Fire Here, 250 Hurt as Crowd Panics," *Baltimore News-Post,* January 30, 1956.
17. Ibid.
18. Ibid.
19. "Church Supper Fire—Panic Brings Death to 11, Injuries Over 200," 316.
20. "10 Dead in Fire Here, 250 Hurt as Crowd Panics," *Baltimore News-Post,* January 30, 1956.
21. Ibid.
22. "10 Burned to Death, 230 Hurt in Fire Here—One Emergency Exit Locked," *Baltimore Sun,* January 30, 1956.
23. Stevens, "Church Oyster Roast Fire Panic," 283.
24. "10 Dead in Fire Here, 250 Hurt as Crowd Panics," *Baltimore News-Post,* January 30, 1956.
25. Stevens, "Church Oyster Roast Fire Panic," 283.
26. "Girl Thrown Out Window," *Baltimore News-Post,* January 30, 1956; 27. "10 Dead in Fire Here, 250 Hurt as Crowd Panics," *Baltimore News-Post,* January 30, 1956.
28. Ibid.
29. Interview with Frank Kvech Jr., 2006.
30. "Church Supper Fire—Panic Brings Death to 11, Injuries Over 200," 316.
31. Interview with Frank Kvech Jr., 2006.
32. John A. Bryan, "A Study of the Survivors Reports on the Panic in the Fire at the Arundel Park in Brooklyn, Maryland, 1/29/56," paper presented at a seminar at the University of Maryland College Park, 1956.
33. Interview with Frank Kvech Jr., 2006.
34. Interview with Joseph and Peg Ross, 2005.
35. "Survivor Says Hall Burned Like Egg Crate," *Baltimore News-Post.* January 30, 1956.
36. "Closed Door Bars Escape Efforts; Many Trampled," *Baltimore Sun,* January 30, 1956.
37. "Brooklyn Barber Credited with Heroic Aid — August Marcellino May Have Crippled Hand from Holocaust," *Maryland Gazette,* February 2, 1956.
38. "Rescue from Burning Building Told by Severna Park Women," *Maryland Gazette,* February 2, 1956.
39. "I Saw a Woman's Face at Window, and Then Her Head Disappeared," *Baltimore Sun,* January 30, 1956.
40. *New York Times,* January 30, 1956; "I Saw A Woman's Face at Window, and Then Her Head Disappeared," *Baltimore Sun,* January 30, 1956.
42. Ibid.

Chapter 7: Black Snow and Crimson Skies

1. Interview with Harry Zlotowski, 2005.
2. Interview with Charlie Doegen, 2005.
3. Ibid.
4. Interview with Joe and Peg Ross, 2005.
5. Interview with Charlie Doegen, 2005.
6. Ibid.
7. Interview with Les Helfrich, 2006.
8. Ibid.
9. Ibid.
10. Ibid.
11. Interview with William Morrison, 2006.
12. Ibid.
13. Ibid.

14. Interview with Gary Utz, 2005
15. Smashing car windows and running hoses through the interiors was portrayed in Ron Howard's 1991 motion picture, *Backdraft*.
16. Interview with Charlie Doegen, 2005.
17. Interview with William Morrison, 2006.
18. Ibid.
19. Ibid.
20. *Combined Report of the Arundel Park Fire*, 6–7.
21. Interview with Brady, Thompson and Feeley, 2008.
22. Interview with Charlie Doegen, 2005.
23. Interview with John Anderson, 2006.
24. Interview with Charlie Doegen, 2005.
25. Interview with Harry Zlotowski, 2005.
26. "10 Dead in Fire Here, 250 Hurt as Crowd Panics," *Baltimore News-Post*, January 30, 1956.
27. Interview with Norman Ray, 2005.
28. Interview with Michael Ripnik, 2006.
29. "10 Die, 250 Hurt as Hall Burns in Brooklyn," *Baltimore Evening Sun*, January 30, 1956.
30. Interview with Michael Ripnik, 2006.
31. "10 Dead in Fire Here, 250 Hurt as Crowd Panics," *Baltimore News-Post*, January 30, 1956.
32. Murray, *Unherald Heros*, 156.
33. "10 Burned to Death, 230 Hurt In Fire Here — One Emergency Exit Locked," *Baltimore Sun*. January 30, 1956.
34. Interview with Frank Homberg, 2005.
35. *Combined Report of the Arundel Park Fire*, attachments.
36. Ibid
37. Interview with Harry Klasmeier, 2006.
38. "10 Dead in Fire Here, 250 Hurt as Crowd Panics," *Baltimore News-Post*, January 30, 1956.
39. Maryland Fire & Rescue Institute, Fire Officer II Curriculum, Lesson 12-1, p. 7, 1999.

Chapter 8: Survivors and Victims
1. "10 Dead in Fire Here, 250 Hurt as Crowd Panics," *Baltimore News-Post*, January 30, 1956.
2. "Horror Seen on Faces Showed They Were Not All Saved," *Maryland Gazette*. February 2, 1956.
3. Ibid.
4. Ibid.
5. Ibid.
6. "10 Dead in Fire Here, 250 Hurt as Crowd Panics," *Baltimore News-Post*, January 30, 1956.
7. Civil Defense Report on the Arundel Park Fire and the Pennsylvania Railroad Train Accident, 1956.* [Hereafter Civil Defense Report.]
8. Ibid.
9. "Doctor Tells of Helping Injured," *Baltimore Evening Sun*, January 30, 1956.
10. Ibid.
11. Civil Defense Report.
12. Ibid.
13. "Doctor Tells of Helping Injured," *Baltimore Evening Sun*, January 30, 1956.
14. Ibid.
15. Civil Defense Report.
16. "Scene of Agony and Despair — Loved Ones Sought by Kin at Hospital," *Baltimore News-Post*, January 30, 1956.
17. Civil Defense Report.
18. "Scene of Agony and Despair — Loves Ones Sought by Kin at Hospital," *Baltimore News-Post*, January 30, 1956.
19. Ibid.
20. Ibid.
21. Ibid.
22. Civil Defense Report.
23. Ibid., 21.
24. Interview with Brady, Thompson and Feeley, 2008.
25. Ibid.
26. Ibid.
27. "Scene of Agony and Despair – Loved Ones Sought by Kin at Hospital," *Baltimore News-Post*, January 30, 1956.
28. Civil Defense Report; 29. Interview with George Mills, 2005.
30. "Marcellino Files $150,000.00 Suit," *Maryland Gazette*, April 12, 1956.

31. "Arundel Park Fire Hero is Eleventh Victim," *Baltimore Sun*, February 5, 1956.
32. Ibid.
33. "10 Dead in Fire Here, 250 Hurt as Crowd Panics," *Baltimore News-Post*, January 30, 1956.
34. Ibid.
35. "The Priest Prayed," *Baltimore News-Post*, January 30, 1956.
36. *Fire Service Bulletin*, University of Maryland Fire Service Extension, May 1956.
37. Ibid.
38. *Combined Report of the Arundel Park Fire*, attachments.
39. "10 Die, 250 Hurt as Hall Burns in Brooklyn," *Baltimore Evening Sun*, January 30, 1956.
40. *Combined Report of the Arundel Park Fire*, 8; interview with Harry Klasmeier, 2005.
42. "Priest Blesses Victims Taken from Fire Scene," *Baltimore Sun*, January 30, 1956.
43. *Combined Report of the Arundel Park Fire*, 8; "10 Dead in Fire Here, 250 Hurt as Crowd Panics," *Baltimore News-Post*, January 30, 1956.
45. "Priest Blesses Victims Taken from Fire Scene," *Baltimore Sun*, January 30, 1956.
46. "10 Dead in Fire Here, 250 Hurt as Crowd Panics," *Baltimore News-Post*, January 30, 1956.
47. Interview with Sonny Tyler and Fred Reppenhagen Jr., 2006.
48. "Fire Aid Trips — Rescue Truck, Ambulances Involved in Crashes," *Baltimore Sun* January 30, 1956.
49. "10 Die, 250 Hurt as Hall Burns in Brooklyn," *Baltimore Evening Sun*, January 30, 1956.
50. Interview with George Mills, 2006.
51. "10 Die, 250 Hurt as Hall Burns in Brooklyn," *Baltimore Evening Sun*, January 30, 1956; interview with Rae (Bathgate) Utz, 2006.
53. Interview with R. McLaughlin, 2007.
54. Ibid.
55. Ibid.
56. Ibid.
57. "Funeral Home is Morgue for Charred Bodies," *Baltimore News-Post*, January 30, 1956.
58. *Combined Report of the Arundel Park Fire*. 1956, p. 8.
59. Ibid.
60. Ibid.
61. "Tribute to Hero of Tragic Fire Paid by House," *Maryland Gazette*. February 8, 1956.
62. Interview with Brady, Thompson and Feeley, 2008.
63. "Tribute to Hero of Tragic Fire Paid by House," *Maryland Gazette*, February 8, 1956.
64. Arundel Park Fire Hero Is Eleventh Victim," *Baltimore Sun*, February 5, 1956.
65. Murray, *Unheralded Heroes*, 156–57.

Chapter 9: Questions, Accusation, and Suspicion

1. Interview with John Hoy, 2006.
2. Ibid.
3. "Behind the Scenes Communications Proved Vital in Sunday Disaster," *Maryland Gazette*, February 2, 1956.
4. Ibid.
5. Ibid.
6. "10 Die, 228 Hurt as Hall Burns in Baltimore," *New York Times*, January 30, 1956.
7. Interview with Harry Klasmeier, 2005.
8. "Shocked and Saddened," editorial, *Maryland Gazette*, February 2, 1956.
9. Ibid.
10. Editorial, *Baltimore News-Post*, January 30, 1956.
11. "Flaming Death," editorial, *Baltimore Sun*, January 30, 1956.
12. Ibid.
13. "Sidewalk Survey," *Maryland Gazette*, February 2, 1956.
14. "Job Well Done," editorial, *Baltimore News-Post*, February 2, 1956.
15. Ibid.

16. Ibid.
17. "Decision on Fire Cause Is Sought by Commissioners," *Baltimore Sun,* January 31, 1956.
18. Ibid.
19. "Two Man Committee Is Named to Conduct an Investigation of Tragic Arundel Fire," *Maryland Gazette*, February 9, 1956.
20. "Investigation Goes On — Arundel Probers Still Seek Witnesses," *Baltimore News-Post,* February 4, 1956.
21. "Stricter Fire Prevention Rules Studied by City," *Baltimore News-Post,* February 2, 1956.
22. "Fire Police Aid at Outing is Urged," *Baltimore Evening Sun* January 31, 1956
23. "County Acts to Bar Fire Hazards," *Baltimore Sun,* February 7, 1956.
24. "Stricter Fire Prevention Rules Studied by City," *Baltimore News-Post,* February 2, 1956.
25. "Fire Probe Begins — Chief Wade Tells Layout of Doomed Hall," *Baltimore News-Post,* January 30, 1956.
26 "Possible Crime Is Checked in Park Fire," *Baltimore Sun,* February 1, 1956; "Stricter Fire Prevention Rules Studied by City," *Baltimore News-Post,* February 2, 1956.
27. "Stricter Fire Prevention Rules Studied By City," *Baltimore News-Post,* February 2, 1956.
30. "Gas Leak Ruled Out in Blaze Fatal to 10," *Baltimore News-Post,* February 2, 1956.
31. "Arundel Board to Consider Fire Case," *Baltimore News-Post,* January 30, 1956.
32. "Trapped — Closed Door Added to Toll," *Baltimore Sun,* January 30, 1956.
33. "Arundel Board to Consider Fire Case." *Baltimore News-Post,* January 30, 1956.
34. "Investigators Hold Theory Fatal Fire Was Accidental — Consider Electrical Defect," *Brooklyn News,* February 8, 1956.
35. "Lowman Reveals Fact — Hall Had Passed Inspection One Month Before Blaze," *Maryland Gazette,* February 9, 1956.
36. "Possible Crime Is Checked in Park Fire," *Baltimore Sun,* February 1, 1956.
37. Isabel Shipley Cunningham, "Little Nevada," *Anne Arundel County History Notes,* 34 (April 2003): 1.
38. Ibid.
39. Ibid.
40. James C. Bradford, *Anne Arundel County Maryland – A Bicentennial History* (Annapolis: Anne Arundel County and Annapolis Bicentennial Committee, 1977). p. 215.
41. Cunningham, "Little Nevada," 3.
42. Bradford, "Anne Arundel County Maryland – A Bicentennial History," 215
43. Cunningham, "Little Nevada," 3.
44. Ibid., 1.
45. Ibid., 4.
46. Ibid.
47. "Mafia Plot Eyed in Fire," *Baltimore News-Post,* February 1, 1956.
48. Ibid.
49. Ibid.
50. "Tribute to Hero of Tragic Fire Paid by House," *Maryland Gazette,* February 8, 1956.

Chapter 10: Investigation

1. "Possible Crime Is Checked in Park Fire," *Baltimore Sun,* February 1, 1956.
2. Interview with William Barnard, 2006.
3. "Possible Crime Is Checked in Park Fire," *Baltimore Sun,* February 1, 1956.
4. Ibid.
5. "Two Man Committee Is Named to Conduct an Investigation of Tragic Arundel Fire," *Maryland Gazette,* February 9, 1956.
6. Ibid.
7. Interview with William Barnard, 2006.
8. "Possible Crime Is Checked in Park Fire," *Baltimore Sun,* February 1, 1956.
9. "Investigators Hold Theory Fatal Fire Was Accidental – Consider Electrical

Defect," *Maryland Gazette,* February 2, 1956.
10. Ibid.
11. Ibid.
12. Ibid.
13. "Investigators Hold Theory Fatal Fire Was Accidental – Consider Electrical Defect," *Maryland Gazette,* February 2, 1956.
14. Ibid.
15. "Two Man Committee Is Named to Conduct an Investigation of Tragic Arundel Fire," *Maryland Gazette,* February 9, 1956.
16. "Stricter Fire Prevention Rules Studied by City," *Baltimore News-Post,* February 2, 1956.
17. "Blame Short in Fire-Probers Praised for Job," *Maryland Gazette,* March 1, 1956.
18. Brophy Report, 2–4.
19. "Thomas Patrick Brophy," *The Police Chief,* September 1955.
20. Thomas Patrick Brophy, "I Solve These Firebug Mysteries," *Saturday Evening Post,* March 5, 12 and 19, 1949.
21. Ibid.
22. Ibid.
23. Ibid.
24. Brophy Report, 2–4.
25. Ibid., 6.
26. Ibid., 16.
27. Ibid., 11.
28. Ibid., 8.
29. Ibid., 16.
30. Ibid., 17.
31. Interview with Harry Klasmeier, 2006.
32. *Combined Report of the Arundel Park Fire.*
33. Ibid.
34. "Blame Short in Fire—Probers Praised for Job," *Maryland Gazette,* March 1, 1956.
35. Ibid.
36. Ibid.
37. Ibid.
38. Ibid.
39. Ibid.
40. Ibid.
41. Ibid.
42. Ibid.
43. Ibid.
44. Ibid.
45. *Combined Report of the Arundel Park Fire,* 26.
46. "Report Finds County Singularly Free from Illegal Gambling, Organized Crime — Outgoing Jury Ask Revision of County Fire Code," *Maryland Gazette,* April 19, 1956.
47. "5 Killed, 100 Hurt in Odenton Wreck of Pennsy Express," *Baltimore News-Post,* February 24, 1956.
48. "Death, Pain, Fear, Cold, Chaos — A Night for Silent Prayer," *Baltimore Sun,* February 24, 1956.
49. Civil Defense Report, 2. The author's copy of this document is missing the front cover and acknowledgments. It is assumed that it was developed under the auspices of the Baltimore Civil Defense organization.
50. Ibid., 19.
51. Ibid., 20–25.
52. Ibid., 2–6.
53. Ibid., 14–15.
54. Ibid., 17–9.
55. Ibid., 24–25.
56. Ibid.
57. Ibid., 35.

Chapter 11: Analysis
1. "Blame Short in Fire—Probers Praised for Job," *Maryland Gazette,* March 1, 1956.
2. "19 Anne Arundel County Schools Branded as Fire Traps," *Baltimore News-Post,* February 8, 1956.
3. Interview with Harry Klasmeier, 2005.
4. Stevens, "Church Oyster Roast Fire Panic," 277–85.
5. Ibid., 285.
6. State of Maryland, *Fire Prevention Code,* Annapolis, 1964.
7. Stevens, "Church Oyster Roast Fire Panic," 285.
8. Brophy Report, 11.
9. Brannigan Francis L., *Building Construction for the Fire Service,* 3rd ed.

(Quincy, Mass.: National Fire Protection Association. 1993), 387.
10. Ibid., 387.
11. Ibid., 387–89.
12. Brophy Report, 1.
13. Interview with Harry Klasmeier, 2005.
14. Lawson, *Beverly Hills Supper Club,* 250.
15. Brannigan, *Building Construction for the Fire Service*, 388.
16. *NFPA News,* March 1955, 5.
17. *NFPA News,* July–August 1955.
18. Stevens, R. E. "Flames Trap 15 in One Story School," *Quarterly of the National Fire Protection Association* (April 1954): 331.
19. "10 Dead in Fire Here, 250 Hurt as Crowd Panics," *Baltimore News-Post,,* January 30, 1956.
20. *Fire Protection Handbook,* 19th ed. (Quincy, Mass.: National Fire Protection Association, 2003), 2-109.
21. Robert Moulton, "Interior Finish for Life Safety from Fire," *Quarterly of the National Fire Protection Association* (July 1961).
22. *NFPA 101: Life Safety Code* (Quincy, Mass.: National Fire Protection Association, 2006): 101–8.
23. Brannigan, *Building Construction for the Fire Service*, 106.
24. Stevens, "Church Oyster Roast Fire Panic," 285.
25. Interview with Frank Kvech, 2005.
26. Stevens, "Church Oyster Roast Fire Panic," 280.
27. *NFPA 101: Life Safety Code,* 101–2.
28. Stevens, "Church Oyster Roast Fire Panic," 278 (Floor Plan).
29. Ibid., 285.
30. Moulton, "Emergency Lighting for Fire Safety," *Quarterly of the National Fire Protection Association* (October 1956): 331. (Note: This excerpt from the October 1956 issue of the *Quarterly* is the only quote by a recognized fire service institution that places the Arundel Park fire with the two deadliest public assembly fires of the twentieth century.)
31. Ibid.
32. *NFPA 101: Life Safety Code,* 101–337.
33. Interview with Harry Klasmeier, 2005.
34. Stevens, "Church Oyster Roast Fire Panic," 278.
35. Interview with Harry Klasmeier, 2005.
36. Stevens, "Church Oyster Roast Fire Panic," 278.
37. *Fire Prevention Code of Anne Arundel County*, 1952.
38. Lawson, *Beverly Hills Supper Club,* 250.
39. *NFPA 101: Life Safety Code,* 101–19.
40. "Employee Emergency Plans," 29 CFR [Code of Federal Regulations] 1910.38 (Davenport, Iowa: Mangan Communications, Inc., 2001).
41. "Blame Short in Fire—Probers Praised for Job," *Maryland Gazette,* March 1, 1956.
42. Stevens, "Church Oyster Roast Fire Panic," 284 (Floor Plan) 284.
43. "Not All Were Heroes, Nor Did All Panic," *Baltimore Evening Sun,* January 30, 1956.
44. Ibid.
45. Combined Report of the Arundel Park Fire, 9.
46. Interview with Joe and Peg Ross, 2005.
47. "Not All Were Heroes, Nor Did All Panic," *Baltimore Evening Sun,* January 30, 1956.
48. "10 Die, 250 Hurt as Hall Burns in Brooklyn," *Baltimore Evening Sun,* January 30, 1956.
49. Combined Report of the Arundel Park Fire, 8–9.
50. Interview with Joe and Peg Ross, 2005.
51. "Beads in Their Hands—Search of Arundel Park Ruins Keepsakes of Victims," *Maryland Gazette,* February 16, 1956.
52. *Fire Protection Handbook,* 19th ed., 4–7.
53. Interview with Frank Kvech, 2006.
54. "Closed Door Bars Escape Efforts; Many Trampled," *Baltimore Sun,* January 30, 1956.
55. Anne Arundel County Building Code, March 1939.

Chapter 12: Black Cloud
1. Stevens, "Church Oyster Roast Fire Panic," 281.
2. Interview with Loretta Kane Dove, 2006.
3. "$150,000 Damages Sought for Death in Fire Tragedy," *Maryland Gazette,* April 1956.
4. "Death Claims Filed in Fire at Park Fete," *Maryland Gazette,* February 1956.
5. Ibid.
6. "Death Catches Up with Augie After Two Hairline Escapes," *Baltimore Sun,* June 6, 1956.
7. "August Seifert, Killed by Truck, Widely Beloved," *Baltimore Sun,* June 6, 1956.
8. "August Siefert Killed While Directing Traffic," *Maryland Gazette,* June 7, 1956.
9. "Church Roof Collapses on 120 at Mass Here—At Least13 Injured; Children Swarm Out of Debris," *Baltimore Sun,* February 9, 1967.
10. Ibid.
11. Ibid.
12. Interview with Brady, Thompson and Feeley, 2008.
13. "Report Calls Church Roof Substandard, Bad Materials, Building Code Violations Cited at Saint Rose of Lima," *Baltimore Sun,* May 24, 1967.
14. "Belle Grove Road Tanker Fire," *Maryland Gazette,* October 5, 1972.
15. Ibid.
16. Ibid.

Chapter 13: Memories and Nightmares
1. "St. Johns, Newfoundland," *Fire Engineering,* January 1942, 23.
2. "San Francisco Social Hall Fire," *Quarterly of the National Fire Protection Association* (October 1964): 103.
3. Interview with Frank Kvech III, 2006.
4. "It Just Went Woosh," *Maryland Gazette,* January 28, 2006.
5. Interview with Rae (Utz) Bathgate, 2006.
6. Interview with Brady, Thompson and Feeley, 2008.
7. Interview with Joe and Peg Ross, 2005.
8. "Beads in Their Hands—Search of Arundel Park Ruins Keepsakes of Victims," *Maryland Gazette,* February 16, 1956.
9. Interview with Joe and Peg Ross, 2005.

Epilogue
1. National Commission on Terrorism Attacks Upon the United States, *The 9/11 Commission Report* (New York: W. W. Norton & Company, 2002), 287–89.

Bibliography

Newspapers

Baltimore News-Post

Baltimore Evening Sun

Baltimore Sun

[Glen Burnie] Maryland Gazette

Official Reports and Documents

Anne Arundel County Building Code. March 1939

Anne Arundel County Police Department, Anne Arundel County Fire Prevention Bureau, Maryland State Police [combined report]. *Report of the Arundel Park Fire*. 1956.

Baltimore Civil Defense Organization Report on Arundel Park Fire and Pennsylvania

Train Wreck. Circa 1956.*

Brophy, Thomas P., Bearnhardt, Abe. *Report on Investigation of Fire at Arundel Park, Anne Arundel County, Maryland.* New York, New York: Private Investigation Report for Arundel Park Corporation. February 15, 1956.

Bryan, John. *A Study of the Survivors Reports on the Panic in the Fire at the Arundel Park in Brooklyn, Maryland, 1/29/56*. College Park, Maryland: University of Maryland, 1956.

Civil Defense Report on the Arundel Park Fire and the Pennsylvania Railroad Train Accident, 1956.

Employee Emergency Plans and Fire Prevention Plans. Washington, D.C: Government Printing Office, 2001. [Code of Federal Regulations. 29 CFR, XII, 1910.38 (July 1, 2001)].

Fire Prevention Code of Anne Arundel County. County Commissioners of Anne Arundel County, 1952.

Klasmeier, Harry. Arundel Park—Fire Prevention Bureau Report. Annapolis, Maryland. March 12, 1955.

National Commission on Terrorism Attacks Upon the United States. *The 9/11 Commission Report.* W. W. Norton & Company. New York, 2002.

Secondary Sources

Bradford, James C. *Anne Arundel County Maryland, A Bicentennial History 1649–1977.* Annapolis, Maryland: Anne Arundel County and Annapolis Bicentennial Committee, 1977.

Brannigan, Francis L. *Building Construction for the Fire Service.* 3rd ed. Quincy, Mass.: National Fire Protection Association, June 1993.

Brooklyn-Curtis Bay Bicentennial Committee. *A History of Curtis Bay and Brooklyn*, 1976.

Bruno, Hal. "Relearning Old Lessons From a Night Club Tragedy." *Firehouse.* New York, New York: March 2006. p.18.

CBS News.com. *Panel Hears of Club Fire Horror.* Associated Press. February 28, 2003.

"Church supper fire-panic brings death to 11, injuries over 200." *Fire Engineering.* April 1956.

Cowan, D., Kuenster, J. *To Sleep With Angels: The Story of a Fire.* Chicago, Ill: Ivan R. Dee, 1996.

Cunningham, Isabel Shipley. "Little Nevada." *Anne Arundel County History Notes.* April 2003.

Fire Officer II Curriculum. Maryland Fire & Rescue Institute, College Park, Maryland, 1999.

Fire Protection Handbook, 18th ed. Quincy, Mass.: National Fire Protection Association, 1997.

Fire Protection Handbook, 19th ed. Quincy, Mass.: National Fire Protection Association, 2003.

Fire Service Extension. *Firemen's Basic.* University of Maryland, 1961.

Kelbaugh, Jack. *The History of Ritchie Highway.* Linthicum, Md.: Anne Arundel County Historical Society, October 1997.

Lawson, R. *Beverly Hills Supper Club: The Anatomy of a Nightclub Fire.* Athens: Ohio University Press, 1984.

Lyons, P. *Fire in America.* Boston: National Fire Protection Association, 1976.

Moulton, Robert. "Interior Finish for Life Safety from Fire." *Quarterly of theNational Fire Protection Association.* July 1961.

Murray, William A. *The Unheralded Heroes of Baltimore's Big Blazes: A Story about Baltimore Firefighters.* Baltimore: E. John Schmitz & Sons, Inc., 1969.

NFPA 101: Life Safety Code. Quincy, Mass.: National Fire Protection Association, 2006.

NFPA News. Quincy, Mass.: National Fire Protection Association. March–August, 1955.

Ray, Norman E., Jr. *Brooklyn Community Volunteer Fire Company Inc.: The Early Years, 1936 –1942.* Brooklyn, Maryland, 2002.

Remember When 1955. Millersville, Tenn.: Seek Publishing, 1956.

"St. Johns, Newfoundland." *Fire Engineering*, January 1942.

"San Francisco Social Hall Fire." *Quarterly of the National Fire Protection Association.* October 1964.

Schneider, Mary Jane. *A Town in Tragedy: The Boyertown Opera House Fire.* Boyertown, Pa.: MJS Publications, 2007.

Sharp, Henry K, *The Patapsco River Valley.* Baltimore: Maryland Historical Society, 2001.

Stevens, R. E. "Church Oyster Roast Fire Panic." *Quarterly of the National Fire Protection Association.* April 1956.

———. "Flames Trap 15 in One-Story School." *Quarterly of the National Fire Protection Association.* April 1954.

Toomey, Daniel Carroll. *A History of Relay, Maryland, and the Thomas Viaduct,* 3rd ed. Baltimore: Toomey Press, 1995.

Travers, Paul J. *The Patapsco: Baltimore's River of History.* Centreville, Md.: Maryland Historical Society–Tidewater Publishers, 1990.

Websites

History of Saint Rose of Lima. [Baltimore: Saint Rose of Lima Catholic Church, 2003.] http://www.stroseparish.org/history.htm.

"Service members' Readjustment Act of 1944." http://www.gibill.va.gov/GI_Bill_Info/history.htm.

Index

Page numbers for illustrations appear in boldface type

ambulances, 25, 82, 87, 92
Amrhein, Donald [Engineman], 74
Anderson, John, Captain [Brooklyn], 73, 79
Anne Arundel Co. Board of Commissioners, 119
Anne Arundel Co., emergency response evaluated, 143, 145
Anne Arundel Co. Police Dept., 106–7, 109, 110, **116, 126**
Anne Arundel Co. Volunteer Firemen's Association, 118
Anne Arundel Co. Fire Prevention Bureau, 30, 150
Anne Arundel Co. Fire Prevention Code, 32, 142
Arbutus Volunteer Fire Dept., **105**
Arthur, Henry T., **24**
Arundel Arena, **181,** 191
Arundel Park, **46**
  and code requirements, 17, 166, 167, 189
  complex described, 10, **11,** 16, **35, 58**
  construction of, 15–16, 166
  disaster strikes again, **168**
  electrical problems, 133, 136
  fire hydrant location, 17, 29, **139**
  at height of the fire, **76–77**
  overhead door and ceiling panels, **51**
  preparations for oyster roast, 16, **45,** 50
Arundel Park Corporation, 15, 131
Arundel Park fire
  assessment of, 57, 60, 117, 135–36, 153, 192–93
  "black snow," 80
  concealed space as location of fire, 58
  deaths and injuries from, 96, 193
  generators, **98, 99**
Arundel Park fire, aftermath, **84–85,** 127, 189, 190
  broken metal casement windows, **128**
  as burned-out shell, **165**
  ruins of milk bar, **89, 160**
Arundel Park fire, and action of firefighters, **79,** 100, 101
Arundel Park fire, described, **66,** 87–88
Arundel Park fire, early response to, 60
Arundel Park fire, injuries treated, 93
Arundel Park fire, investigated, 129–30, 137, **142,** 143, 149
Arundel Park fire, property damage estimates, 169, **170**
Arundel Park fire, rapidity of destruction from, 191
Arundel Park fire and World Trade Center tragedy, 193–94

Baltimore City Fire Alarm Office, 82
Baltimore City Fire Commissioners, 115
Baltimore City Fire Dept., 41
Baltimore Civil Defense agency, 144–45
Baltimore News-American, **176**
Baltimore News-Post, **112,** 113, 115, 117, 122
Baltimore Sun, fire as arson, 118–19
Belle Grove Rd., 7, 9, 56, 87, 91, 187–88
Belle Grove Road, and housing boom, 10, **11,** 25
Bierman, Leonard [Ferndale firefighter], **106**
Board of Fire Underwriters, 23
Bowen, Julia [Nurse], 91
Bracken, Gerald F., U.S. Marshal, **121**
Brady, Andrew, Jr. [A.A.Co. Police Dept.]
  assists firefighters, 97
  and belief fire was of criminal origin, 186
  and father's death, 107, 186
Brady, Andrew, Sr. [Special Police Officer], **125**
  attempts to extinguish fire in kitchen wall, 60
  burn injuries deemed too severe, 78, 96
  dies from severe burns, 100, 107, 109
  ensures no one left behind, 100, 193
  resolution honoring, 124–25, **125**
  retired Baltimore City firefighter, 26, 36–37, 41
  and work at Arundel Park, 42, 53, 55
Brady, Edith, 41
Brady, John "Bill," 53, 96
Brandt, Anna and Mary, 59, 62, 164
Brooklyn, 12, 20, 39
Brooklyn Community Volunteer Fire Dept., 5, **22,** 39
  as "Brooklyn VFD Fire Station," 21, **22,** 23, 26
  engines of, **4, 6, 20, 22,** 23, **27**
  formation of, 19, 23
Brooklyn Fire Dept., 40
  and growth of community, 24, 25
  equipment of, 25, **27,** 40
  as progressive in firefighter training, 28

volunteers replaced with professional crews, 20
Brooklyn Park, 10, 24, 25, **72,** xv
Brophy, Thomas Patrick, 131, 132, **133**
and causes and nature of back draft, 134, 135–36
as chief fire marshal of NYCFD, 131–32
fire report findings, 132–33, 135–37
Brown, William L., Jr., **24**
Bryan, John L., [Prof.], 65
Bureau of Fire Underwriters, 32

Cavanaugh, Stella, victim, 164
Civil Defense Agency, recommendations of, 146
Civil Defense Agency, report of
collision, automobile and tanker truck, **178, 179**
beneath I-895 bridge, 177–78, **178–80**
and centralized fire alarm dispatch center, 180–82
heat of fire buckles steel I-beams, 182
Cooke, Frances, 60, 163, 193

delayed alarm, 58, 59
Doegen, Charles [Vol. Lieutenant]
accompanies Utz in US open-cab pumper, 69
sees flames coming from back of building, 70
pulls down smoldering ceiling with pike pole, **81**
radios second and third alarms, 75
takes initial phone call from Arundel Park, 72–73
Dove, Loretta Kane, 169
Dulaney, Elizabeth
60, 61, 163, 187, **190**
Dulaney, James, 60, 61, 163, **190**

Ecker, Charles [Baltimore City Fire Dept.]
attacks flames in ceiling, 61
off-duty firefighter, 28, 59
opens trapdoor, burned by fireball, 60
picks up fire extinguisher, 59
suffers severe burns, 61
emergency assistance, provision of
fire dept. ladies auxiliaries, Salvation Army, 103
emergency vehicles
engines, ladder trucks, rescue, ambulances, 83
employment
shipyards, shipping terminals, rail yards, airport, 26
Engines
Ahrens-Fox, **18, 41**
American Eagle "Spartan," used at I-895 fire, 182
Brooklyn #2, 8
Engine #1, the "US," **6,** 6–8, **21, 70,** 73
Engine #17, Ahrens-Fox Fire Pumper, 41
Engine #21, Brooklyn, 82
Engine #26, 41
Andrew Brady's old company, at fire, 107
Engine #35, 20, 173
Engine #1 and two-way radio, 24
Engine #2 [Brooklyn], the "Mack," second to arrive, 4, **71,** 73
Engine #10 [Fairfield], 82
Engine #35 of Brooklyn, 43
Engine #57 of Curtis Bay, 43
Engine #26 [West Street], 82
Ferndale pumper at front of building, 75
Linthicum VFD Ford pumper, **71,** 75, 78
"Little Mack" from Linthicum VFD, **73**
Mack pumper, 73
"Reo" Rescue truck, "Rescue Hose" Company of Annapolis, 102
Evans, Albert
separated from wife, 62
Evans, Frederick [Brooklyn VF Co]
repeated trips to hospital as ambulance driver, 82, 91
Everd, John M. , A.A. Co. Commissioner, escapes and helps from outside, 68
Eyerly, Warren, and Max Muller, transport for blood donors, 110
Eyerly, Warren, dispatcher, AACPD, handles radio traffic among crews, 110

Faubert, Gustave H. "Gus," Dr. and identification of victims, 103, 104
Feeley, George [nephew to Andrew Brady], 42, 55, 61
Ferndale, MD
as location of country police department, 25
fiberboard, hazards of, 153–55
File, Jim, 69
fire, acceleration of
due to falling ceiling tile, 60
due to opening of overhead door, 60
due to opening of trap door, 60
fire, aftermath of, **126**
Arundel Park Hall, **124**
fire
alarm deemed unnecessary, 56
alarm sent, 69
departures begin, 59–60
escape from, 86, 87
injured treated at area hospitals, 97
seen moving toward main hall, 57
fire, investigation of, 118, 127
national and local organizations assist in, 129

questions and accusations regarding, 109, 114
rumors regarding causes of, 117
special committee assigned to investigate, 130
task force of government agencies, 124
witnesses interviewed, 130
fire, major factors in
chairs and tables, 161
despite existing code, no announcement, 161–62
employees untrained in emergency procedures, 161–62
fire department not called immediately, 161
guests not evacuated immediately, 161
lack of fire alarm system, employee training, 161
fire, memories of 87
fire, newspaper coverage of
as "blackened tragedy" in *Baltimore Sun,* 111–13
News-Post coverage as "flaming death," **112,** 113
fire, progression of
families separated, 62
lights out and panic, 63
sequence of events, 139–40
trap door and raging fire, 61–62
fire, spread of, ix
fire aftermath
cloak room, clothing removed from, **111**
fireplace outside of kitchen, **151**
Fire Alarm Dispatch Center, 147
fire companies, assistance of, 83
fire department, and two-way radio, 25
fire engines, 48, 83
fire extinguishers, types of, 35–36, 162
fire hydrant, insufficient to fight fire, 75
fire investigation
carbon monoxide as cause of deaths, 141, 165
and county fire prevention code, 143
and delay in calling Brooklyn Fire Dept., 141
electrical ventilation systems detailed, 132–33
failure to evacuate building as cause of death, 142
findings of, 139–40
locked doors as causing "fatal delay," 140–41
fire investigation, NFPA
Harry Klasmeier and Richard Stevens as members, 138
fire marshal, duties of, 32, 33
fire protection, 21
fires, tragedy of delayed alarms, 57
fire safety
early alarm, importance of, 57
early alarm notification and evacuation procedures rarely done, 162
and early evacuation of occupants, 57
importance of reliable equipment, 32
and need for well-trained firefighters, 32
not limited to fire department or officials, 194
as partnership with community, 194
sprinklers and fire-alarm systems, 161
fire safety awareness
importance of, x
Fire Service Extension program, 49
fire stations, 20, **20,** 32
First response, Brooklyn fire station
Les Helfrich, John Anderson, Norman Ray, 73
Fisher, Russell S. [Medical Director], 105
flames burst from ceiling, 60
Flax, Leonard, Dr.
advise ambulances re: which hospitals to go to, 92
advise injured but not critical not to go to hospitals immediately, 92
aids 75 victims, 91
establishes aid station and treats wounded, 91
performs triage and administer morphine to burned, 91
uses bandages alcohol, iodine from ambulance and engine first aid, 92
Ford, Edgar, [Volunteer Engineman], 75
Fort George G. Meade, 102
Franczkowski, Josephine, victim, 164
Friendship Airport Fire Dept., 27, 83

gambling, legalized, 119
Gleim, [Det. AAPD], 143
Governor Ritchie Highway, **8,** 9
Great Baltimore Fire, 3
Griffith, Robert W. [Police Officer], 87

Hagner, Elmer [AA Co.Police Sergeant], 105
Hanover Street drawbridge, 13, **14**
Harbor Tunnel Throughway, 171, 177
Harrison, James K., 30
Hasse, Ron, **29, 69**
Helfrich, Lester
connects hose to hydrant, 74
and flames rolling up back of main hall, 73
as officer, driver, and fire training instructor, 29
pumper driver, **49**
teaching basic firefighting class, 49–50, 69
Helms, Roy, 10–12, 13, 15, **171**
allegedly approached by organized crime, 123

calls fire dept., 59
notices hall's neon lights off, 133–34
opens trap door and sees smoldering fire, 59
as part owner of Arundel Park Corporation, 123
returns to hall, 44
sees flames burst through ceiling, 61
shuts off gas supply, 58
Helms, William, 134–35, 136
Helms Cocktail Lounge, 13, 15
Hevener, John H., 118
Heying, Theodore, [B.C.F.D.], 135
Holy Name Society, 44
Homburg, Frank, Jr.
works at fire until late, 82–83
Homburg, Frank E.,"Old Fire Horse," **4**, 9
Brooklyn Park pump operator, 82
as Engineman and Deputy Chief, **4**, 9, **28**, 50
as "fire chauffeur" and pump operator, 23, 24
instructor, engineman, deputy chief, 28–29, 33
notes embers from fire land more than mile and a half away, 80
Hoy, John [Volunteer, Ferndale VFC], 109
Hubers, Willie [Engineman, Ferndale VFC], 74, 109
Jager, Joseph, 23, 63, 74, 97
Janaskie, Thomas
helps more than 30 women to exits, 62
Johnson, Charles, 56
Junker, Harry, 19

Kelly, Liston, and wife Theresa, 62, 163
Klasmeier, Harry
as AA Co.'s first fire marshal, **18**, 31, 32, 33
on cause of fire, 133, 150–52
chief fire marshal appointed head of investigation, 129
conducts inspection of the interior, 34–35, 36
and Fire Underwriters Rating Bureau report, 137–38
and investigation conclusions, 138–39, 143, 150–51
and adoption of safety code, 150
plans fire inspection of Arundel Park hall, 30
starts to conduct a full evaluation of the exterior, 33–34
Kozlowski, Stella, 60, 163, 186–87, 187, 190, **190**, 193
Kvech, Frank, III [son of Frank Jr.]
persistence of caution in, 185
searches for and finds father, 66
sees no panic; helps patrons evacuate, 61
witnesses no panic, 157
Kvech, Frank, Jr. [father of Frank III]
releases bent door latch, 65
opens the overhead door, 140
refusal to discuss fire years later, 185
releases lock and opens overhead door, 165–66
saved hundreds of lives, 164
as volunteer cook at the event, 52

Ladies Auxiliary, Brooklyn Fire Dept., 103, 186
Life Safety Code, 152
Light Street Toll Bridge, 12, **13, 14**
Linthicum fire station, 74

Marcellino, August, 67, 97
Maryland Gazette, 86, 113, **114,** 186
Maryland House of Delegates
adopts resolution honoring Andrew Brady Sr., 124–25
Maryland State Firemen's Association, 23
Maryland State Police, staff of, **126**
Matlack Trucking Company, 10, **11, 124,** 182–83, **183**
McKay, Gladys, victim, 164
McKinley, John, [Capt.], 82
McLaughlin, Randall, Dr., 103, 104
media
and death of H. L. Mencken, 110–111
filmed rushed to station and broadcast, 96, 102–103
London Times calls for information, 110
trampling by panicked guests, **65,** 156
medical care providers, 91
Mencken, H. L. , death of, 110–111
Mercy Hospital, **94, 97**
Middlekrauf, Bob, 134
milk bar, **90, 148**
Morrison, Will, 75
Muller, Max, [Sergeant AACPD], 110
Myers, August C., former State Delegate, 82

National Fire Protection Association (NFPA)
codes more stringent than those of county, 142
and fire protection standards, 149, 150
Neil, Joseph W., 21
New York Times, 11
NFPA Life Safety Code, 157, 162
NFPA Quarterly, 155–56

O'Brien, Lawrence, on brutality of panicked patrons, 63
obstacles hindering firefighters, 70, 72, 73, 74

Obzut, Frances, 60, 163
Obzut, Monette, 64
Occupational Health and Safety Administration
requirement to develop emergency plans, 162
organized crime, suggested as source of fire, 122–24
Otto, Goldie, victim, 164
overhead door, west wall, **164,** 165–66

panic, 61, 86
and crowd behavior, 63, 64, 65
Patapsco River area, 5, 10, 26, 90
Pennsylvania Railroad car, derailment of, 143–45, **144, 145**
Phipps, Nelson [Volunteer rescue truck driver], 102
Puenke, Martin [Captain, Md. State Police], 105
Pumphrey, 10

Ray, Norman [Volunteer, Brooklyn Fire Dept.], 79–80
Red Cross, 93, 146
Ripnick, Gordon, 15, 80
Ripnick, Michael, and "black snow," 16
Ripnick, Richard, 16
Ripple, Father Leonard J., 40, 43, 44
Robertson, H. Charles, 123–24, 141, 143
Ross, Joe, 70, **190**
and Arundel Park fire, 187–88, 189–91
Ross, Peg, 70, 187 189, **190**
Rust, Leo, 67

safety codes, 157, 159, 160, 161
Saint Rose of Lima Church, 37, **38,** 39–40, 42–43, 44
history of fires, 40, 43
oyster roast, 50–51
priests of, 47
programs and missions of, 41
Saint Rose of Lima Church, roof collapse of, 173, **174–75, 176**
causes identified, 177
field hospital, 173
firefighters, police aid in rescue, 173, **176, 177**
Secoura, John, 56
Seifert, August [Special Police Officer], 100, 171–73
Sinai Hospital, 92
slot machines, 11, **120, 123**
and organized crime, 120, 121
confiscated, **122**
Smith, Harry [*Maryland Gazette*], 86
Smith, Thomas [Detective, MDSP]
and investigation of fire, **126,** 127–28, 143
rating bureau as uncooperative, 138
rushes to derailment, 143
as state police superintendent, 127
smoke, first notice of, 56
Sokolis, Louise (Lou), 52
badly shaken by fire, 90, 184–85
injuries of, 92, 93
knocked over, 62, 65, 164
persistence of fear and caution in, 184–85
Sokolis, Wally, 80–82, 100, 184
South Baltimore General Hospital
control point set up to identify patients, 93
emergency room, **95, 95**
presence of media adds to chaos, 96
special police officers, 93
staff efforts, 92, 93
victims treated, 92, **94, 95,** 96
Spiegel, Uncle Frank
and memory of Arundel Park fire, 189
Stevens, Richard NFPA
and combustibles in concealed attic, 153–57
deaths due to evacuation and alarm delays, 152–53
fails to mention locked exits, 158
identifies major factors, 141–43, 152
survivors, 67, 87
Swinimer, James, 180, 181

Testermann, Brack [Corporal], 105
Thomas, James "Jimmy" [center alarm operator], 180–81
Thompson, John "Jerry," 42
train derailment, lessons learned from, 144, 145, 147
Tribull, John, [priest] St. Michael's Church, 101

Underwriters' Laboratories, 155
University of Md. Fire Service Extension program, **28,** 49
Utz, Ed, [Engineman] 31, 33, **48**
Division Chief and fire alarm dispatch center, 180
assists at fire, 69, 72, 74

victims, 101, 102, 104

Wade, Wilbur C., [Chief, AACPD]
believed there had been two fires, **116,** 116–17
fire as worst disaster in Anne Arundel Co. history, 117
rushes to derailment, 143
Walterhoefer, William, 59, 61
Washington Post, **108**

Yenger, Ralph [Brooklyn VFD], 130, **131**

Zlotowski, Harry, 69, 185–86
Zylka, Walt, 57

Division Chief Joseph B. Ross Jr., CPFS, retired in 2000 after 33 years with the Anne Arundel County (Maryland) fire department. He has served on the faculty of the University of Maryland, Maryland Fire and Rescue Institute, written extensively for fire prevention journals and is currently a Fire Program Specialist with the U.S. Fire Adminisration. He resides with his wife Kathy in Linthicum, Maryland, near where the events described in Arundel Burning occurred.